D. H. LAWRENCE

SELECTED POEMS

ALSO BY D. H. LAWRENCE

NOVELS

Sons and Lovers
The Rainbow
Women in Love
The Lost Girl
Aaron's Rod
Kangaroo
Lady Chatterley's Lover
Four Short Novels (Love among the Haystacks, The Ladybird, The Fox, The Captain's Doll)

NONFICTION

Twilight in Italy
Psychoanalysis and the Unconscious and *Fantasia of the Unconscious*
Sea and Sardinia
Studies in Classic American Literature
Apocalypse
Etruscan Places
Sex, Literature, and Censorship

COLLECTIONS

Phoenix
The Portable D. H. Lawrence
The Complete Short Stories of D. H. Lawrence
Selected Literary Criticism
The Collected Letters of D. H. Lawrence
The Complete Poems of D. H. Lawrence
The Complete Plays of D. H. Lawrence
Phoenix II

D. H. LAWRENCE

SELECTED POEMS

with an introduction by Kenneth Rexroth

THE VIKING PRESS · NEW YORK

VIKING COMPASS EDITION
Issued in 1959 by The Viking Press, Inc.
625 Madison Avenue, New York, N. Y. 10022

Distributed in Canada by
The Macmillan Company of Canada Limited

Eleventh printing June 1969

This collection is also published by New Directions in the clothbound New Classics Series.

Printed in the U.S.A. by The Colonial Press, Inc.

CONTENTS

ALPHABETICAL LIST OF POEMS

D. H. LAWRENCE

SELECTED POEMS

INTRODUCTION

At the very beginning Lawrence belonged to a different order of being from the literary writers of his day. In 1912 he said: "I worship Christ, I worship Jehovah, I worship Pan, I worship Aphrodite. But I do not worship hands nailed and running with blood upon a cross, nor licentiousness, nor lust. I want them all, all the gods. They are all God. But I must serve in real love. If I take my whole passionate, spiritual and physical love to the woman who in turn loves me, that is how I serve God. And my hymn and my game of joy is my work. All of which I read in . . ."

Do you know what he read all that in? It makes you wince. He thought he found that in *Georgian Poetry, 1911–1912!* In Lascelles Abercrombie, Wilfred Gibson, John Drinkwater, Rupert Brooke, John Masefield, Walter de la Mare, Gordon Bottomley! What a good man Lawrence must have been. It is easy to understand how painful it was for him to learn what evil really was. It is easy to understand why the learning killed him, slowly and terribly. But he never gave up. He was always hunting for comradeship—in the most unlikely places—Michael Arlen, Peter Warlock, Murry, Mabel Dodge. He never stopped trusting people and hoping. And he went on writing exactly the gospel he announced in 1912, right to the end.

Lawrence thought he was a Georgian, at first. There are people who will tell you that his early poetry was typical Georgian countryside poetry—*Musings in the Hedgerows*, by the Well Dressed Dormouse. It is true that early poems like *The Wild Common* (page 25), *Cherry Robbers* (page 27), and the others, bear a certain resemblance to the best Georgian verse. They are rhymed verse in the English language on "subjects taken from nature." Some of the Georgians had a favorite literary convention. They were anti-literary. Lawrence was the real thing. His "hard" rhymes, for instance. "quick-kick, rushes-pushes, sheepdip-soft lip, gudgeon-run on." I don't imagine that when Lawrence came to "soft lip" he remembered that bees had always sipped at soft lips and that, as a representative of a new tendency it was up to him to do something about it. I think his mind just moved in regions not covered by the standard associations of standard British rhyme patterns. At the end of his life he was still talking about the old sheep dip, with its steep soft lip of turf, in the village where he was born. Why, once he even rhymed wind and thinned, in the most unaware manner imaginable. That is something that, to the best of my knowledge, has never been done before or since in the British Isles.

The hard metric, contorted and distorted, and generally banged around, doesn't sound made up, either. Compulsion neurotics like Hopkins and querulous old gentlemen like Bridges made quite an art of metrical eccentricity. You turned an iamb into a trochee here, and an anapest into a hard spondee there, and pretty soon you got something that sounded difficult and tortured and intense. I think Lawrence was simply very sensitive to quantity and to the cadenced pulses of verse. In the back of his head was a stock of sundry standard English verse patterns. He started humming a poem, hu hu hum, hum hum, hu hu hum hu, adjusted it as best might be to the remembered accentual patterns, and let it go at that. I don't think he was unconscious of the new qualities which emerged, but I don't think he went about it deliberately, either.

This verse is supposed to be like Hardy's. It is. But there is always something a little synthetic about Hardy's rugged verse. The smooth ones seem more natural, somehow. The full dress, Matthew Arnold sort of sonnet to Leslie Stephen is probably Hardy's best poem. It is a very great poem, but Arnold learned the trick of talking like a highly idealized Anglican archbishop and passed it on to Hardy. That is something nobody could imagine Lawrence ever learning, he just wasn't that kind of an animal.

Hardy could say to himself: "To-day I am going to be a Wiltshire yeoman, sitting on a fallen rock at Stonehenge, writing a poem to my girl on a piece of wrapping paper with the gnawed stub of a pencil," and he could make it very convincing. But Lawrence really was the educated son of a coal miner, sitting under a tree that had once been part of Sherwood Forest, in a village that was rapidly becoming part of a worldwide, disemboweled hell, writing hard, painful poems, to girls who carefully had been taught the art of unlove. It was all real. Love really was a mystery at the navel of the earth, like Stonehenge. The miner really was in contact with a monstrous, seething mystery, the black sun in the earth. There is a vatic quality in Lawrence that is only in Hardy rarely, in a few poems, and in great myths like *Two on a Tower.*

Something breaks out of the Pre-Raphaelite landscape of *Cherry Robbers.* That poem isn't like a Victorian imitation of medieval illumination at all. It is more like one of those crude Coptic illuminations, with the Christian content just a faint glaze over the black, bloody "babylonian turbulence" of the Gnostic mystery. I don't know the date of the *Hymn to Priapus* (page 60), it seems to lie somewhere between his mother's death and his flight with Frieda, but it is one of the Hardy kind of poems, and it is one of Lawrence's best. It resembles Hardy's *Night of the Dance.* But there is a difference. Hardy is so anxious to be common that he just avoids being commonplace. Lawrence *is* common, he doesn't have to try. He is coming home from a party, through the winter fields, thinking of his dead mother, of the girl he has just had in the barn, of his troubled love life, and suddenly Orion leans down out of the black heaven and touches him on the thigh, and the hair of his head stands up.

Hardy was a major poet. Lawrence was a minor prophet. Like Blake and Yeats, his is the greater tradition. If Hardy ever had a girl in the hay, tipsy on cider, on the night of Boxing Day, he kept quiet about it. He may have thought that it had something to do with "the stream of his life in the darkness deathward set," but he never let on, except indirectly.

Good as they are, there is an incompleteness about the early poems. They are the best poetry written in England at that time, but they are poems of hunger and frustration. Lawrence was looking for completion. He found it later, of course, in Frieda, but he hadn't found it then. The girl he called Miriam wrote a decent, conscientious contribution to his biography. She makes it only too obvious that what he was looking for was not to be found in her. And so the Miriam poems are tortured, and defeated, and lost, as though Lawrence didn't know where he was, which was literally true.

Between Miriam and Frieda lies a body of even more intense and troubled poems. Those to his mother, the dialect poems, and the poems to Helen are in this group. The 'mother' poems are amongst his best. (See pages 50–52.) They are invaluable as direct perspectives on an extraordinary experience.

From one point of view Lawrence is the last of a special tradition that begins with St. Augustine and passes through Pascal and Baudelaire amongst others, to end finally in himself. There is no convincing evidence for Freud's theory that the Oedipus Complex dates back to some extremely ancient crime in the history of primitive man. There is ample evidence that Western European civilization is specifically the culture of the Oedipus Complex. Before Augustine there was nothing really like it. There were forerunners and prototypes and intimations, but there wasn't the real thing. The *Confessions* introduce a new sickness of the human mind, the most horrible pandemic and the most lethal ever to afflict man. Augustine did what silly literary boys in our day boast of doing. He invented a new derangement. If you make an intense effort to clear your mind and then read Baudelaire and Catullus together, the contrast, the new thing in Baudelaire, makes you shudder. Baudelaire is struggling in a losing battle with a ghost more powerful than armies, more relentless than death. I think it is this demon which has provided the new thing in Western Man, the insane dynamic which has driven him across the earth to burn and slaughter, loot and rape.

I believe Lawrence laid that ghost, exorcised that demon, once for all, by an act of absolute spiritual transvaluation. *Piano* (page 55), *Silence* (page 50), *The Bride* (page 49), and the other poems of that period, should be read with the tenth chapter of the ninth book of the *Confessions*. It is the beginning and the end. Augustine was a saint. There are acts of salvation by which man can raise himself to heaven, but, say the Japanese, a devil is substituted in his place. Lawrence drove out the devil, and the man stepped back. Or, as the Hindus say, with an act of absolute devotion from the worshipper, the goddess changes her aspect from maleficent to benign.

It is not only that Lawrence opened the gates of personal salvation for himself in the 'mother' poems. He did it in a special way, in the only way possible, by an intense realization of total reality, and by the assumption of total responsibility for the reality and for the realization. Other people have tried parts of this process, but only the whole thing works.

This shows itself in these poems, in their very technique. There, for the first time, he is in full possession of his faculties. He proceeds only on the basis of the completely real, the completely motivated, step by step along the ladder of Blake's "minute particulars." Ivor Richards' *Practical Criticism* contains a symposium of his students on Lawrence's *Piano* (page 55). It makes one of the best introductions to Lawrence's poetry ever written. And one of the qualities of his verse that is revealed there most clearly is the uncanny, "surreal" accuracy of perception and evaluation. Objectivism is a hollow word beside this complete precision and purposiveness.

From this time on Lawrence never lost contact with the important thing, the totality in the particular, the responsibility of vision. Harrassed by sickness and betrayal, he may have faltered in fulfilling that most difficult of all the injunctions of Christ, to suffer fools gladly. He may have got out of contact with certain kinds of men at certain times. He may have become cross and irritable and sick. But he never lost sight of what really mattered: the blue vein arching over the naked foot, the voices of the fathers singing at the charivari, blending in the winter night, Lady Chatterley putting flowers in Mellors' hair.

The 'Helen' poems are strange. (See *A Winter's Tale*, page 48; *Return; Kisses in the Train; Under the Oak*, page 54; *Passing Visit To Helen*, page 55; *Release*, page 53; *Seven Seals*, page 58). They all have a weird, dark atmosphere shot through with spurts of flame, a setting which remained a basic symbolic situation with Lawrence. It is the atmosphere of the pre-War I novel, young troubled love in gaslit London—draughty, dark, and flaring, and full of mysterious movement. Probably the girl's name was not Helen. Lawrence thought of her as dim, larger than life, a demigoddess, moving through the smoke of a burning city. For certain Gnostics Helen was the name of the incarnate "female principle," the power of the will, the sheath of the sword, the sacred whore who taught men love. Helen seems to have been the midwife of Lawrence's manhood. At the end, something like her returns in the Persephone of *Bavarian Gentians* (page 136). Re-birth. No one leaves adolescence cleanly without a foretaste of death.

Ezra Pound said that the dialect poems were the best thing Lawrence ever wrote. This is just frivolous eccentricity. But they are fine poems, and in them another figure of the myth is carefully drawn. They are poems about Lawrence's father, the coal miner who emerges nightly from the earth with the foliage of the carboniferous jungles on his white body. Lawrence's little dark men, his Gypsies, and Indians, and Hungarians, and Mexicans, and all the rest, are not dark by race, but dark with coal dust. The shadow of forests immeasurably older than man has stained their skins. Augustine was never at peace until he found his father again in the pure mental absolute of Plotinus. Lawrence found his father again in the real man, whose feet went down into the earth. In certain poems where he speaks as a fictional woman, the erotic intensity is embarassing to those of us who still live in the twilight of the Oedipus Complex. What had been evil in the father image becomes a virtue, the source of the will; deep behind the mother image lies the germ of action, the motile flagellate travelling up the dark hot tube seeking immortality.

The boy watching the miners rise and descend in the yawning maw of the earth in Nottinghamshire grows into the man of forty watching the Indians pass in and out of a lodge where an old man is interminably chanting—there is a sense of strangeness, but no estrangement. There is no effort to violate the mystery of paternity because it is known in the blood. Lawrence knew by a sort of sensual perception that every cell of his body bore the marks of the striped Joseph's coat of the paternal sperm.

All this world of the early poems, and of the novels, *The White Peacock*, *The Trespasser*, the first draft of *Sons and Lovers*, is an unborn world, a cave, a womb, obscure and confused. The figures have a mythic vagueness about them. The sensual reality seems to be always struggling beneath an inhibiting surface of flesh, struggling to escape into another realm of meaning. So many of the images are drawn from birth, escape, confinement, struggle. Critics have found much of their Freudianism in the work of this period. Had they been better read they would have found Jung above all else, and certainly Rank. Lawrence had yet to read Freud or Jung and may never have heard of Rank.

Some shockingly ill-informed things have been written about Lawrence's relation to psychoanalysis. In the first place, he was not a Freudian. He seems to have read little Freud, not to have understood him any too well, and to have disliked him heartily. In the winter of 1918–1919 he read Jung, apparently for the first time, in English. Presumably this was *The Psychology of the Unconscious.* Jung was very much in the air in those days, as he is again. There was probably a great deal of amateur talk about his ideas amongst Lawrence's friends. But Lawrence does not seem to have had much more to go on, and *The Psychology of the Unconscious* is only the beginning of the system later elaborated by Jung. Nor did he ever become intimate with any of his students. Later Mabel Dodge tried to bring them together by correspondence. The story goes that Jung ignored her letters because they were written in pencil. So much for that.

Lawrence wrote quite a bit on psychoanalysis. There are the two books, *Psychoanalysis and the Unconscious,* a somewhat sketchy popularization of some of Jung's basic concepts, and *Fantasia of the Unconscious,* of which, more in a moment. And then there are the reviews of Trigant Burrow's book, and miscellaneous remarks scattered through correspondence and reviews. This is all of the greatest importance to the understanding of Lawrence.

Fantasia of the Unconscious is an extraordinary book. It is foully written, unquestionably Lawrence's worst writing, but it is certainly a landmark in the history of psychoanalysis. It is an attempt to combine the empirical neurology of Kundalini Yoga with his own interpretation of Jung's psychology and with a theory of sexuality which may be either his own or derived from popular, occultist expositions of certain Gnostic sects and rumors of the practices of Shakti-Yoga. When it appeared, it must have seemed like pure fantasy of the Lost Atlantis variety. Jung's *Secret of the Golden Flower*, and his studies of "spiritual alchemy" lay in the future. The "psychology of the autonomic system" was unheard of. It is all there, in Lawrence's inspired guesses. The white race is going mad, but it is the autonomic nervous system which is out of kilter; what goes on in the head is secondary—and the autonomic nervous system is, as a whole, the organ of communion.

To return to the poems. There is an hallucinatory quality in the images of the poems which precede Frieda which it is interesting to compare with the induced hallucination of H.D. The conflict in H.D. is hidden in herself. It is still there to this day, although her latest prose work has been the journal of a Freudian analysis. Her images are purified of conflict, then the intensity which has been distilled from the sublimation of conflict is applied from the outside. ("Your poetry is not pure, eternal, sublimated," she told Lawrence). What results is a puzzling hallucination of fact, a contentless mood which seems to reflect something tremendously important but whose mystery always retreats before analysis.

Lawrence's early poems are poems of conflict. The images are always polarized. Antagonisms struggle through the texture. But the struggle is real. The antagonisms are struggling towards the light. The conflict yields to insight, if not to analysis. It is like the propaedeutic symbolism of the dream, as contrasted to the trackless labyrinths of falsification which form the patterns of most waking lives. The hallucination is real, the vision of the interior, personal oracle. Its utterance has meaning, more meaning than ordinary waking reality because the subjective is seen in the objective, emerging from it, the dream from the reality—not dislocated or applied from outside the context.

The poems of *Look! We Have Come Through!* fall into three groups. First there are the structurally more conventional pieces like *Moonrise* (page 59), which sounds a little like Masefield's sonnets though it is incomparably finer, and the *Hymn to Priapus* (page 60), and the others—they are all probably earlier and have already been discussed. Second, there are the poems of the Rhine Journey, *December Night* (page 70), *New Year's Eve* (page 70), *Coming Awake* (page 71), *History* (page 73); erotic epigrams, intense as Meleager, more wise than Paul the Silentiary. Lawrence was still a young man, and had many great poems to write—but put these beside the few poets who have survived from that day, Sturge Moore, Monro, De La Mare, they look like pygmies. Only Yeats stands up against Lawrence. And last, there are the Whitmanic free verse manifestoes, "explaining" marriage to a people who had forgotten what it was.

With Frieda the sleeper wakes, the man walks free, the "child" of the alchemists is born. Reality is totally valued, and passes beyond the possibility of hallucination. The clarity of purposively realized objectivity is the most supernatural of all visions. Bad poetry always suffers from the same defects: synthetic hallucination and artifice. Invention is not poetry. Invention is defense, the projection of pseudopods out of the ego to ward off the 'other.' Poetry is vision, the pure act of sensual communion and contemplation.

That is why the poems of Lawrence and Frieda on their Rhine Journey are such great poetry. That is why they are also the greatest imagist poems ever written. Reality streams through the body of Frieda, through everything she touches, every place she steps, valued absolutely, totally, beyond time and place, in the minute particular. The swinging of her breasts as she stoops in the bath, the roses, the deer, the harvesters, the hissing of the glacier water in the steep river—everything stands out lit by a light not of this earth and at the same time completely of this earth, the light of the Holy Sacrament of Marriage, whose source is the wedded body of the bride.

The accuracy of Lawrence's observation haunts the mind permanently. I have never stood beside a glacier river, at just that relative elevation, and just that pitch, with just that depth of swift water moving over a cobbled bed, without hearing again the specific hiss of Lawrence's Isar. These poems may not be sublimated (whatever Y.M.C.A. evasion that may refer to) but they are certainly pure and eternal.

Again, it is fruitful to compare the Rhine Journey poems

with the only other poems of our time which resemble them much, Ford Madox Ford's *Buckshee.* Ford was writing about something very akin to what Lawrence was, about an aspect of marriage. But he was writing about its impossibility, about how life had bled away its possibility from both him and his girl, and how they had taken, in middle age and in the long Mediterranean drouth, the next best thing—intense erotic friendship. And about how, every once in a while, marriage comes and looks in at the window. The contrast with Lawrence and Frieda, sinking into the twilight in the fuming marsh by the Isar, "where the snake disposes," is pathetic past words.

Ford's *L'Oubli—Temps de Secheresse* and Lawrence's *River Roses* (page 66) and *Quite Forsaken* (page 68) are things of a kind and the best of their kind, but like the north and south poles, there is all the difference in the world between them. There is more communion in Frieda's temporary absence than in the closest possible kiss "under the catalpa tree, where the strange birds, driven north by the drouth, cry with their human voices." "Singular birds, with their portentuous, singular flight and human voices" says Ford. This is the Persephone of *Bavarian Gentians* (page 136) and the Orphic birds which flutter around the dying who are withdrawing themselves, corpuscle by corpuscle, from communion. Lawrence would come there one day, with the dark blue flowers on the medicine table and Frieda sleeping in a chair beside him, but he was on the other side of the universe then—the early summer of 1912, in the Isartal, the snow leaving the mountains.

After the Rhine Journey come the poems of struggle for a living adjustment. The ceremonial glory of the sacrament passes from the forefront of consciousness and the period of adjustment to the background of life begins. Every detail of life must be transformed by marriage. This means creative conflict on the most important level.

Sacramental communion is bound by time. Mass does not last forever. Eventually the communicant must leave the altar and digest the wafer, the Body and Blood must enter his own flesh as it moves through the world and struggles with the devil. The problem lies in the sympathetic nervous system, says Lawrence. And it is not easy for two members of a deranged race, in the Twentieth Century, to learn again how to make those webs mesh as they should.

Some of these poems are, in a sense, Frieda's—records of her own interior conquest. It is amazing how much they accomplished, these two. Today, revisiting this battlefield between love and hate that is so carefully mapped in certain of the poems, it is like Gettysburg, a sleepy, pastoral landscape dotted with monuments and graves. Only maimed women and frightened men are Suffragettes anymore. Hedda Gabbler is dead, or lurking in the suburbs. We should be grateful to Frieda. It was she who gave the dragon its death blow, and the Animus no longer prowls the polls and bedrooms, seeking whom it may devour.

The Whitmanic poems seem to owe a good deal to *Children of Adam* and *Calamus*. They look like Whitman on the page. But if read aloud with any sort of ear, they don't sound much like him. Whitman flourished in the oratorical context of Nineteenth Century America. He isn't rhetorical in the invidious sense, that is, there is nothing covert or coercive about him. He says what he means, but he says it in the language of that lost art of elocution so popular in his day. There is little of this in Lawrence. At this period his long-lined free verse is derived almost entirely from the poetry of the Bible, the Psalms, the song of Deborah, the song of Hezekiah, of

Moses, the Benedicite, the Magnificat, the Nunc Dimittis. All the devices of Hebrew poetry are there, and in addition, the peculiar, very civilized, self-conscious "sympathetic" poetry of St. Luke—those poems which have made his the "women's Gospel," and which all good Englishmen must learn in childhood as part of the Morning and Evening Prayer of the Church.

In the volume *Look! We Have Come Through!* Lawrence was just beginning to learn to write free verse. I don't think some of the poems are completely successful. They are diffuse and longwinded. He tries to say too much, and all at the same pitch of intensity; there are no crises, no points of reference. On the whole the most successful is *New Heaven and Earth* (page 75). It may not be a perfect object of art but it is a profound exhortation.

Beyond Holy Matrimony lies the newly valued world of birds, beasts, and flowers—a sacramentalized, objective world. "Look, we have come through"—to a transformed world, with a glory around it everywhere like ground lightning. The poems of *Birds, Beasts, and Flowers* have the same supernatural luster that shines through the figures of men and animals and things, busy being part of a new redeemed world, as they are found carved around the mandala of the Blessed Virgin above some cathedral door or on some rose window.

Birds, Beasts, and Flowers is the mature Lawrence, in complete control of his medium, or completely controlled by his demon. He never has any trouble. He can say exactly what he wants to say. Except for the death poems, he would never write better. (And too, after this, he would never be well again.) He seems to have lived in a state of total realization—the will and its power, positive and negative, at maximum charge, and all the universe streaming between them glowing and transformed. The work of art grows in that electric field, is a "function" of it. It is the act of devotion in the worshipper that forces the god to occupy the statue. It is the act of devotion in the sculptor that forces the god to occupy the stone which the artist then pares to his invisible limbs, tailors like cloth. It is never theology in the first; it is never aesthetics or any teachable craft in the second. The craft is the vision and the vision is the craft.

Good cadenced verse is the most difficult of all to write. Any falsity, any pose, any corruption, any ineptitude, any vulgarity, shows up immediately. In this it is like abstract painting. A painting by Mondriaan may look impersonal enough to be reduced to code and sent by telegraph. Maybe. But it offers no refuge, no garment, no mask, no ambush, for the person. The painter must stand there, naked, as Adam under the eye of God. Only very great or very trivial personalities dare expose themselves so.

Think of a few typical writers of cadenced verse, Whitman, Sandburg, Wallace Gould, F. M. Ford, F. S. Flint, Aldington, Lola Ridge, and James Oppenheim. (H.D.'s verse is primarily a counterpointing of accentual and quantitative rhythms in patterns of Greek derivation. Pound's verse is Latin in reference, and usually quantitative.) How the faults stand out! Every little weakness is revealed with glaring cruelty. Whitman's tiresome posturing, Sandburg's mawkishness, Aldington's erotic sentimentality, the over-reaching ambition of Lola Ridge and Oppenheim—what a lot of sore thumbs standing out! Yet in many ways these are good poets, and Whitman is a very great one.

Gould, Flint and Ford were never dishonest, never overreached themselves, did their best to say what they meant and no more, never bargained with art. "The sentimentalist," said

Daedalus, "is he who would enjoy, without incurring the immense debtorship for a thing done." They are not prophets, but they are good poets because they rendered a strict accounting with their own souls.

Sentimentality is spiritual realization on the installment plan. Socially viable patterns, like conventional verse, are a sort of underwriting or amortization of the weaknesses of the individual. This is the kernel of sense in the hollow snobbery of Valéry. The sonnet and quatrain are like the national debt, devices for postponing the day of reckoning indefinitely. All artistic conventions are a method of spiritual deficit-financing. If they were abandoned, the entire credit structure of Poets, Ltd. would be thrown into hopeless confusion. It is just as well that the professors have led the young, in my lifetime, away from free verse to something that can be taught. No one could be taught to be Lawrence, but in a world where the led lead the leaders, those who might pretend to do so are sure to be confidence men.

Lawrence's free verse in *Birds, Beasts, and Flowers* is amongst the small best ever written. It can be analysed, but the paradigms produced by the analysis are worthless. It cannot be explained away, demonstrated in a mathematical sense. Neither, certainly, can any other great poetry; but at least a convincing illusion can be created, and the young can be provided with something to practice. A poem like *Bat* (page 93), or *St. Mark* (page 83), moves with a stately, gripping sonority through the most complex symphonic evolutions. The music is a pattern of vibration caught from the resonant tone of Lawrence himself. The concerto is not on the page, little spots with flags and tails on a stave, but the living thing, evolving from the flesh of the virtuoso. It is like Gregorian chant or Hindu music, one thing when sung at

Solesmes, or in the ruins of Konarak, another when "rendered" by the Progressive Choral Group or at a concert of the Vedanta Society of Los Angeles.

Again, the faults of *Birds, Beasts, and Flowers* are the excess of virtue. Like anyone who knows he has something intensely important to say, Lawrence found it hard to keep from being longwinded. I think a good deal of his over-expansiveness and repetition is due to his methods of composition.

Some poets meditate in stillness and inactivity, as far away as possible from the creative act. We know that Baudelaire and T. S. Eliot, by their own testimony, spent long periods of time quiescent, inert as artists, turning over and over the substance of vision within themselves. Sometimes, as in Baudelaire, this process is extremely painful, a true desert of the soul. Months went by in which the paper and pen were red hot, it was impossible for him to read, his whole personality seemed engulfed in a burning neurasthenia. And then there would come a period of peace, and slowly growing exaltation, and finally the creative act, almost somnambulistic in its completion. Actual composition by this sort of personality tends to be rare, and usually as perfect as talent permits.

Lawrence meditated pen in hand. His contemplation was always active, flowing out in a continuous stream of creativity which he seemed to have been able to open practically every day. He seldom reversed himself, seldom went back to re-work the same manuscript. Instead, he would lay aside a work that dissatisfied him and re-write it all from the beginning. In his poetry he would move about a theme, enveloping it in constantly growing spheres of significance. It is the old antithesis: centrifugal versus centripetal, Parmenides versus Heraclitus. He kept several manuscript books of his verse and whenever he wanted to publish a collection he would go through them and pick out a poem here and there, the ones he considered had best handled their themes. Behind each poem was usually a group of others devoted to the same material. His selection was always personal, and sometimes it was not very "artistic." *Nettles,* for instance, is a selection of what are, by any standard, the poorer poems of the collections of epigrams printed in *Last Poems.*

There are those who think these epigrams, the ones in *Pansies,* and those in *Last Poems,* aren't art. This opinion is the product of a singular provincialism. It is true that, due to the reasons just mentioned, they aren't all successful, but they belong to a tradition, are members of a species, which has produced some of the greatest poetry. Epigram or maxim, Martial or La Rochefoucauld, the foundations of this tradition are far more stable than those of the neo-metaphysical poetry produced, with seven ambiguities carefully inserted in every line, by unhappy dons between the wars.

Any bright young man can be taught to be artful. It is impossible to teach taste, but you can teach most anybody caution. It is always the lesser artists who are artful, they must learn their trade by rote. They must be careful never to make a false step, never to speak out of a carefully synthesized character. The greatest poetry is nobly dishevelled. At least, it never shows the scars of taking care. "Would he had blotted a thousand lines," said Ben Jonson of Shakespeare. Which thousand? Lawrence was always mislaying those manuscript books of poetry and writing around the world for them, just as Cézanne left his paintings in the fields. Not for any stupid reason—that they were not Perfect Works of Art—but simply because he forgot.

Eliot (who does not write that way), writing of Pound's epigrams, points out that the major poet, unlike the minor, is always writing about everything imaginable, and so, is in good form for the great poem when it comes. Practice makes perfect, and those who wait for the perfect poem before putting pen to paper may wait mute forever. I suppose it is the absolutism which has swept over popular taste in the wake of Cubism which has encouraged the ignorant to expect a canzone of Dante's in each issue of their favorite little magazine, a School of Athens in every WPA mural. This is just greediness, like children who want it to be Christmas every day. And it produces an empty, pretentious, greedy art. Meanwhile, Pound's *Les Millwin*, and Lawrence's *Willy Wet-Legs* quietly preëmpt immortality, a state of being only rarely grandiose.

As far as I know the poems in the novel *The Plumed Serpent* (see pages 122–130) have never been printed separately. This book is one of the most important (he thought it the most important) Lawrence ever wrote. It has brought forth all sorts of pointless debate. People are always saying: "Well, I have lived in Mexico for years and it *simply* isn't like that." Lawrence was not an idiot. He knew it wasn't. And in the first chapter he gave a very accurate and pitiful picture of the 'real' Mexico, sterile, subcolonial, brutal, with the old gods gone, and the church gone, and the revolution a swindle, and nothing left but a squalid imitation of Ashtabula, Ohio. And he knew the other side too, the pasty frigid nymphomaniacs, the deranged women of Europe and America, who consider themselves disciples of Lawrence and prowl the earth seeking Dark Gods to take to bed. He wrote a story which should have destroyed them forever—*None of That.* It should be read with *The Plumed Serpent.*

Every year there is less, but in Lawrence's day there was still something, of the primeval Mexico—at the great feast in Oaxaca, in the life of the peasants in the remote villages, in the Indian communities in the back country. Lawrence did not make any very definite contact with the ancient Mexico but he could see and sense it, and he was fresh from a much less-touched primitive world—that of the Navaho and Pueblo Indians of the Southwest. His materials were not as abundant as they might have been but they were enough to build a book of ritual, of the possible that would never be, of potentialities that would never emerge. It is a book of ceremonial prophecy, but prophecy uttered in the foreknowledge it would never be fulfilled.

The re-awakening of mystery, the revival of the old Aztec religion, the political "Indianism"—even if it all came true, one knows it would be a fraud, a politician's device, as Indianism is in Latin America today. Lawrence knew that, of course, and so the book is dogged with tragedy. One constantly expects the characters to go out in a blazing Götterdämmerung in some dispute with the police, like a gangster movie. They don't, but maybe it would have been better if they had, for eventually they tire; they seem to become secretly aware that all this gorgeous parading around in primitive millinery, this Mystery, and Fire, and Blood, and Darkness, has been thought up. There is something Western European, British Museum, about it. The protagonist, Kate, submits to her lover's insistent Mystery, but rather out of ennui and loathing of Europe than out of any conviction, and one feels that the book could have no sequel, or only a sequel of disintegration, like *Women in Love.*

Still, in the middle of the book, before the fervor dies out, Lawrence wrote as nearly as he could what be believed should be. If the religion of Cipriano and Ramon is taken as an otherworldly system of values, it is profound and true, and, due to the freshness of its symbols, tremendously exciting. Also, it differs very little from any other religion that has maintained its contacts with its sources. Ramon and Cipriano short-circuit themselves where Christianity was short-circuited by Constantine, in the desire to have both worlds, to found a political religion—a Church. That, if any, is the "message" of the book.

The mystery survives in the poems, just as the sacraments survived Constantine. They are not the greatest poems Lawrence ever wrote, but they are amongst the most explicit. This is Lawrence's religion. Wherever he found it he is now in complete possession of a kind of orthodoxy, the orthodoxy of the heterodox—the symbolic world of the Gnostics, the Occultists, Tantrism, Jung. In a sense they are failures, these poems, in the way that the Indian songs published by the United States Bureau of Ethnology are not failures. But, again, that is the message of the book. Finally you discover that you cannot make up paganism. What you make up is a cult. There is nothing primitive about Gnosticism, anymore than there is anything primitive about Theosophy. It is the creation of over-civilized Hellenistic intellectuals. Tantrism too grew up in India, in Buddhism and Hinduism, when civilization was exhausting itself. Jung comes, with Lawrence, at the end of the career of Western European Man. Lawrence, after all, was a contemporary of Niels Bohr and Picasso. And so his poems are mystical poems—and the Aztecs were not mystics, they were just Aztecs. This doesn't invalidate the poems. They have very little to do with ancient or modern Mexico but they do express, very well, the personal religion of D. H. Lawrence. They may be full of "occult lore," but behind the machinery is an intense, direct, personal, mystical apprehension of reality.

In the last hours Lawrence seems to have lived in a state of suspended animation, removed from the earth, floating, transfigured by the onset of death. Poems like *Andraitix—Pomegranate Flowers* (page 113) have an abstracted, disinterested intensity, as though they were written by a being from another planet. Others are short mystical apothegms. There is no millinery anymore, no occultism, they differ only in their modern idiom from any and all of the great mystics. And finally there are the two death poems, *Bavarian Gentians* (page 136), and *The Ship of Death* (page 138). Each was written over several times. There exists a variant which can be taken as a final, or pre-final, version of *Bavarian Gentians*, but both are clusters of poems rather than finished products.

The Ship of Death material alone would make a small book of meditations, a contemporary *Holy Dying*. It is curious to think that once such a book would have been a favorite gift for the hopelessly ill. Today people die in hospitals, badgered by nurses, stupefied with barbiturates. This is not an age in which a "good death" is a desired end of life.

All men have to die, and one would think a sane man would want to take that fact into account, at least a little. But our whole civilization is a conspiracy to pretend that it isn't going to happen—and this, in an age when death has become more horrible, more senseless, less at the will of the individual than ever before. Modern man is terribly afraid of sex, of pain, of evil, of death. Today childbirth, the ultimate orgiastic experience, has been reduced to a meaningless dream; dentists insist on injecting novocaine before they clean your teeth; the agonies of life have retreated to the source of life. Men and women torture each other to death in the bedroom, just as the dying dinosaurs gnawed each other as they copulated in the chilling marshes. Anything but the facts of life. Today you can take a doctor's degree in medicine or engineering and never learn how to have intercourse with a woman or repair a car. Human self-alienation, Marx called it. He said that was all that was really wrong with capitalism. "Let us live and lie reclined" in a jet-propelled, streamlined, air-cooled, lucite incubator. When we show signs of waking, another cocktail instead of the Wine of God. When we try to break out, flagellation instead of Holy Matrimony, psychoanalysis instead of Penance. When the machinery runs down, morphine for Extreme Unction.

In a world where death had become a nasty, pervasive secret like defecation or masturbation, Lawrence re-instated it in all its grandeur—the oldest and most powerful of the gods. The *Ship of Death* poems have an exaltation, a nobility, a steadiness, an insouciance, which is not only not of this time but which is rare in any time. It doesn't matter who: Jeremy Taylor, the Orphic Hymns, the ancient Egyptians—nobody said it better. And there is one aspect of *The Ship of Death* which is unique. Lawrence did not try to mislead himself with false promises, imaginary guarantees. Death is the absolute, unbreakable mystery. Communion and oblivion, sex and death, the mystery can be revealed—but it can be revealed only as totally inexplicable. Lawrence never succumbed to the temptation to try to do more. He succeeded in what he did do.

Kenneth Rexroth

THE WILD COMMON

The quick sparks on the gorse-bushes are leaping
Little jets of sunlight texture imitating flame;
Above them, exaltant, the peewits are sweeping:
They have triumphed again o'er the ages, their screamings
proclaim.

Rabbits, handfuls of brown earth, lie
Low-rounded on the mournful turf they have bitten down to
the quick.
Are they asleep?—are they living?—Now see, when I
Lift my arms, the hill bursts and heaves under their spurting
kick!

The common flaunts bravely; but below, from the rushes
Crowds of glittering king-cups surge to challenge the blos-
soming bushes;
There the lazy streamlet pushes
His bent course mildly; here wakes again, leaps, laughs, and
gushes

Into a deep pond, an old sheep-dip,
Dark, overgrown with willows, cool, with the brook ebbing
through so slow;
Naked on the steep, soft lip
Of the turf I stand watching my own white shadow quivering
to and fro.

What if the gorse-flowers shrivelled, and I were gone?
What if the waters ceased, where were the marigolds then,
and the gudgeon?

What is this thing that I look down upon?
White on the water wimples my shadow, strains like a dog on a string, to run on.

How it looks back, like a white dog to its master!
I on the bank all substance, my shadow all shadow looking up to me, looking back!
And the water runs, and runs faster, runs faster,
And the white dog dances and quivers, I am holding his cord quite slack.

But how splendid it is to be substance, here!
My shadow is neither here nor there; but I, I am royally here!
I am here! I am here! screams the peewit; the may-blobs burst out in a laugh as they hear!
Here! flick the rabbits. Here! pants the gorse. Here! say the insects far and near.

Over my skin in the sunshine, the warm, clinging air
Flushed with the songs of seven larks singing at once, goes kissing me glad.
You are here! You are here! We have found you! Everywhere
We sought you substantial, you touchstone of caresses, you naked lad!

Oh but the water loves me and folds me,
Plays with me, sways me, lifts me and sinks me, murmurs: Oh marvellous stuff!
No longer shadow!—and it holds me
Close, and it rolls me, enfolds me, touches me, as if never it could touch me enough.

Sun, but in substance, yellow water-blobs!
Wings and feathers on the crying, mysterious ages, peewits
wheeling!
All that is right, all that is good; all that is God takes sub-
stance! a rabbit lobs.
In confirmation, I hear sevenfold lark-songs pealing.

CHERRY ROBBERS

Under the long dark boughs, like jewels red
In the hair of an Eastern girl
Hangs strings of crimson cherries, as if had bled
Blood-drops beneath each curl.

Under the glistening cherries, with folded wings
Three dead birds lie:
Pale-breasted throstles and a blackbird, robberlings
Stained with red dye.

Against the haystack a girl stands laughing at me,
Cherries hung round her ears.
Offers me her scarlet fruit: I will see
If she has any tears.

TWILIGHT

Darkness comes out of the earth
And swallows dip into the pallor of the west;

From the hay comes the clamour of children's mirth;
  Wanes the old palimpsest.

The night-stock oozes scent,
  And a moon-blue moth goes flittering by;
All that the worldly day has meant
  Wastes like a lie.

The children have forsaken their play;
  A single star in a veil of light
Glimmers; litter of day
  Is gone from sight.

LOVE ON THE FARM

What large, dark hands are those at the window
Grasping in the golden light
Which weaves its way through the evening wind
  At my heart's delight?

Ah, only the leaves! But in the west
I see a redness suddenly come
Into the evening's anxious breast—
  'Tis the wound of love goes home!

The woodbine creeps abroad
Calling low to her lover:
  The sun-lit flirt who all the day
  Has poised above her lips in play
  And stolen kisses, shallow and gay

Of pollen, now has gone away—
She woos the moth with her sweet, low word;
And when above her his moth-wings hover
Then her bright breast she will uncover
And yield her honey-drop to her lover.

Into the yellow, evening glow
Saunters a man from the farm below;
Leans, and looks in at the low-built shed
Where the swallow has hung her marriage bed.
The bird lies warm against the wall.
She glances quick her startled eyes
Towards him, then she turns away
Her small head, making warm display
Of red upon the throat. Her terrors sway
Her out of the nest's warm, busy ball,
Whose plaintive cry is heard as she flies
In one blue swoop from out of the sties
Into the twilight's empty hall.

Oh, water-hen, beside the rushes,
Hide your quaintly scarlet blushes,
Still your quick tail, lie still as dead,
Till the distance folds over his ominous tread!

The rabbit presses back her ears,
Turns back her liquid, anguished eyes
And crouches low; then with wild spring
Spurts from the terror of his oncoming;
To be choked back, the wire ring
Her frantic effort throttling:
Piteous brown ball of quivering fears!
Ah, soon in his large, hard hands she dies,

And swings all loose from the swing of his walk!
Yet calm and kindly are his eyes
And ready to open in brown surprise
Should I not answer to his talk
Or should he my tears surmise.

I hear his hand on the latch, and rise from my chair
Watching the door open; he flashes bare
His strong teeth in a smile, and flashes his eyes
In a smile like triumph upon me; then careless-wise
He flings the rabbit soft on the table board
And comes toward me: he! the uplifted sword
Of his hand against my bosom and oh, the broad
Blade of his glance that asks me to applaud
His coming! With his hand he turns my face to him
And caresses me with his fingers that still smell grim
Of rabbit's fur! God, I am caught in a snare!
I know not what fine wire is round my throat;
I only know I let him finger there
My pulse of life, and let him nose like a stoat
Who sniffs with joy before he drinks the blood.

And down his mouth comes to my mouth! and down
His bright dark eyes come over me, like a hood
Upon my mind! his lips meet mine, and a flood
Of sweet fire sweeps across me, so I drown
Against him, die, and find death good.

LETTER FROM TOWN: THE ALMOND TREE

You promised to send me some violets. Did you forget?
  White ones and blue ones from under the orchard hedge?
  Sweet dark purple, and white ones mixed for a pledge
Of our early love that hardly has opened yet.

Here there's an almond tree—you have never seen
  Such a one in the north—it flowers on the street, and I stand
  Every day by the fence to look up at the flowers that expand
At rest in the blue, and wonder at what they mean.

Under the almond tree, the happy lands
  Provence, Japan, and Italy repose;
  And passing feet are chatter and clapping of those
Who play around us, country girls clapping their hands.

You, my love, the foremost, in a flowered gown,
  All your unbearable tenderness, you with the laughter
  Startled upon your eyes now so wide with hereafter,
You with loose hands of abandonment hanging down.

WEDDING MORN

The morning breaks like a pomegranate
  In a shining crack of red;
Ah, when tomorrow the dawn comes late
  Whitening across the bed
It will find me at the marriage gate
  And waiting while light is shed

On him who is sleeping satiate
  With a sunk, unconscious head.

And when the dawn comes creeping in,
  Cautiously I shall raise
Myself to watch the daylight win
  On my first of days,
As it shows him sleeping a sleep he got
  With me, as under my gaze
He grows distinct, and I see his hot
  Face freed of the wavering blaze.

Then I shall know which image of God
  My man is made toward;
And I shall see my sleeping rod
  Or my life's reward;
And I shall count the stamp and worth
  Of the man I've accepted as mine,
Shall see an image of heaven or of earth
  On his minted metal shine.

Oh, and I long to see him sleep
  In my power utterly;
So I shall know what I have to keep. . . .
  I long to see
My love, that spinning coin, laid still
  And plain at the side of me
For me to reckon—for surely he will
  Be wealth of life to me.

And then he will be mine, he will lie
  Revealed to me;

Patent and open beneath my eye
  He will sleep of me;
He will lie negligent, resign
  His truth to me, and I
Shall watch the dawn light up for me
  This fate of mine.

And as I watch the wan light shine
  On his sleep that is filled of me,
On his brow where the curved wisps clot and twine
  Carelessly,
On his lips where the light breaths come and go
  Unconsciously,
On his limbs in sleep at last laid low
  Helplessly,
I shall weep, oh, I shall weep, I know
  For joy or for misery.

LIGHTNING

I felt the lurch and halt of her heart
  Next my breast, where my own heart was beating;
And I laughed to feel it plunge and bound,
And strange in my blood-swept ears was the sound
  Of the words I kept repeating,
Repeating with tightened arms, and the hot blood's blind-fold
    art.

Her breath flew warm against my neck,
  Warm as a flame in the close night air;

And the sense of her clinging flesh was sweet
Where her arms and my neck's blood-surge could meet.
  Holding her thus, did I care
That the black night hid her from me, blotted out every speck?

I leaned me forward to find her lips,
  And claim her utterly in a kiss,
When the lightning flew across her face,
And I saw her for the flaring space
  Of a second, afraid of the clips
Of my arms, inert with dread, wilted in fear of my kiss.

A moment, like a wavering spark,
  Her face lay there before my breast,
Pale love lost in a snow of fear,
And guarded by a glittering tear,
  And lips apart with dumb cries;
A moment, and she was taken again in the merciful dark.

I heard the thunder, and felt the rain,
  And my arm fell loose, and I was dumb.
Almost I hated her, she was so good,
Hated myself, and the place, and my blood,
  Which burned with rage, as I bade her come
Home, away home, ere the lightning floated forth again.

BABY RUNNING BAREFOOT

When the white feet of the baby beat across the grass
The little white feet nod like white flowers in a wind,

They poise and run like puffs of wind that pass
Over water where the weeds are thinned.

And the sight of their white playing in the grass
Is winsome as a robin's song, so fluttering;
Or like two butterflies that settle on a glass
Cup for a moment, soft little wing-beats uttering.

And I wish that the baby would tack across here to me
Like a wind-shadow running on a pond, so she could stand
With two little bare white feet upon my knee
And I could feel her feet in either hand

Cool as syringa buds in morning hours,
Or firm and silken as young peony flowers.

AWARE

Slowly the moon is rising out of the ruddy haze,
Divesting herself of her golden shift, and so
Emerging white and exquisite; and I in amaze
See in the sky before me, a woman I did not know
I loved, but there she goes, and her beauty hurts my heart;
I follow her down the night, begging her not to depart.

A WHITE BLOSSOM

A tiny moon as small and white as a single jasmine flower
Leans all alone above my window, on night's wintry bower,

Liquid as lime-tree blossom, soft as brilliant water or rain
She shines, the first white love of my youth, passionless and in
    vain.

AFTER THE OPERA

Down the stone stairs
Girls with their large eyes wide with tragedy
Lift looks of shocked and momentous emotion up at me.
And I smile.

Ladies
Stepping like birds with their bright and pointed feet
Peer anxiously forth, as if for a boat to carry them out of the
    wreckage;
And among the wreck of the theatre crowd
I stand and smile.
They take tragedy so becomingly;
Which pleases me.

But when I meet the weary eyes
The reddened, aching eyes of the bar-man with thin arms,
I am glad to go back to where I came from.

WHETHER OR NOT

I

Dunna thee tell me it's his'n, mother,
  Dunna thee, dunna thee!

—Oh ay, he'll come an' tell thee his-sèn,
  Wench, wunna he?

Tha doesna mean ter say ter me, mother,
  He's gone wi' that—
—My gel, owt'll do for a man i' th' dark;
  Tha's got it flat!

But 'er's old, mother, 'er's twenty year
  Older nor him—
—Ay, an' yaller as a crowflower; an' yet i' th' dark
  Er'd do for Tim.

Tha niver believes it, does ter, mother?
  It's somebody's lies.
—Ax 'im thy-sèn, wench; a widder's lodger!
  It's no surprise.

II

A widow o' forty-five
Wi' a bitter, dirty skin,
To ha' 'ticed a lad o' twenty-five,
An' 'im to 'ave been took in!

A widow of forty-five
As 'as sludged like a horse all 'er life
Till 'er's tough as whit-leather, to slive
Atween a lad an' 'is wife!

A widow of forty-five!
A glum old otchel, wi' long
Witch teeth, an' 'er black hawk-eyes, as I've
Mistrusted all along!

An' me as 'as kep' my-sèn
Shut like a daisy bud,
Clean an' new an' nice, so's when
He wed he'd ha'e summat good!

An' 'im as nice an' fresh
As any man i' th' force,
To ha' gone an' given his clean young flesh
To a woman that coarse!

III

You're stout to brave this snow, Miss Stainwright,
  Are you makin' Brinsley way?
—I'm off up th' line to Underwood
  Wi' a dress as is wanted to-day.

Oh, are you goin' to Underwood?
  'Appen then you've 'eered!
—What's that as 'appen I've 'eered on, Missis?
  Speak up, you nedn't be feared.

Why, your young man an' Widow Naylor,
  'Er as 'e lodges wi'!

They say he's got 'er wi' childt; but there
  It's nothing to do wi' me!

Though if it's true, they'll turn 'im out
  O' th' p'lice force, without fail;
An' if it's *not* true, you may back your life
  They'll listen to *her* tale.

—Well, I'm believin' no tale, Missis,
  I'm seein' for my-sèn.
An' when I know for sure, Missis,
  I'll talk *then.*

IV

Nay, robin red-breast, tha nedna
  Sit noddin' thy head at me!
My breast's as red as thine, I reckon.
  Flayed red, if tha could but see.

Nay, yo' blessed pee-whips,
  Yo' nedna scraight at me!
I'm scraightin' my-sèn, but arena goin'
  Ter let iv'rybody see.

Tha *art* smock-ravelled, bunny,
  Larropin' neck an' crop
I' th' snow! but I's warrant thee
I'm further ower th' top.

V

Now sithee theer at th' reelroad crossin'
Warmin' 'is-sèn at the stool o' fire
Under th' tank as fills th' ingines,
If there isn't my dearly-beloved liar!

My constable, wi' 'is buttoned breast
As stout as the truth, my Sirs! an' 'is face
As bold as a robin! It's much he cares
For this nice old shame an' disgrace.

Oh, but 'e drops 'is flag when 'e sees me!
Yi, an' 'is face goes white! Oh yes,
Tha can stare at me wi' thy fierce blue eyes;
Tha won't stare me out, I guess.

VI

Whativer brings thee out so far
  In a' this depth o' snow?
—I'm takin' 'ome a weddin'-dress,
  If yer mun know.

Why, is there a weddin' at Underwood
  As tha ne'd trudge up 'ere?
—It's Widder Naylor's weddin'-dress,
  'Er'll be wantin' it, I 'ear.

'Er doesna want no weddin'-dress—
  Why—? but what dost mean?
—Doesn't ter know what I mean, Timmy?
  Yi, tha must ha' bin 'ard ter wean!

Tha'rt a good-un at suckin'-in yet, Timmy!
  But tell me, isn't it true
As 'er'll be wantin' my weddin'-dress
  In a wik or two?

—That's no 'casions ter ha'e me on,
  Lizzie; what's done is done.
—*Done*, I should think so! An' might I ask
  When tha begun?

It's thee as 'as done it, as much as me,
  So there, an' I tell thee flat.
—Me gotten a childt ter thy landlady?
  —Tha's gotten thy answer pat.

As tha allus 'ast; but let me tell thee
  Hasna ter sent me whoam, when I
Was a'most burstin' mad o' my-sèn,
  An' walkin' in agony?

After I'd kissed thee at night, Lizzie,
  An' tha's laid against me, an' melted
Into me, melted right into me, Lizzie,
  Till I was verily swelted.

An' if my landlady seed me like it,
  An' if 'er clawkin' eyes

Went through me as the light went out,
  Is it any cause for surprise?

—No cause for surprise at all, my lad;
  After kissin' an' cuddlin' wi' me, tha could
Turn thy mouth on a woman like that!
  I hope it did thee good.

—Ay, it did; but afterwards
  I could ha' killed 'er.
—Afterwards! how many times afterwards
  Could ter ha' killed 'er?

Say no more, Liz, dunna thee;
  'Er's as good as thee.
—Then I'll say good-bye to thee, Timothy;
  Take 'er i'stead o' me.

I'll ta'e thy word good-bye, Liz,
  Though I shonna marry 'er.
Nor 'er nor nub'dy.—It is
  Very brave of you, Sir!

—T' childt maun ta'e its luck, it mun,
  An' 'er maun ta'e *'er* luck.
F'r I tell yer I h'arena marryin' none
  On yer; yo'n got what yer took!

—That's spoken like a man, Timmy,
  That's spoken like a man!
" 'E up an' fired 'is pistol,
  An' then away 'e ran!"

—I damn well shanna marry 'er,
  Nor yo', so chew it no more!
I'll chuck the flamin' lot o' you—
  —Yer nedn't 'ave swore!

VII

There's 'is collar round th' candlestick,
An' there's the dark-blue tie I bought 'im!
An' these is the woman's kids 'e's so fond on,
An' 'ere comes the cat as caught 'im!

I dunno wheer 'is eyes was—a gret
Round-shouldered hag! My Sirs, to think
Of 'im stoopin' to 'er! You'd wonder 'e could
Throw 'imself down *that* sink!

I expect yer know who I am, Mrs. Naylor?
  —Who y'are? yis, you're Lizzie Stainwright.
An' 'appen you'd guess then what I've come for?
  —'Appen I mightn't, 'appen I might.

Yer knowed as I was courtin' Tim Merfin?
  —Yis, I knowed 'e wor courtin' thee.
An' yet yer've bin carryin' on wi' 'im!
  —Ay, an' 'im wi' me.

Well, now yer've got ter pay for it.
  —If I han, what's that ter thee?
'E isn't goin' ter marry yer.
  —Tha wants 'im thy-sèn, I see.

It 'asn't nothin' to do with me.
  —Then what art colleyfoglin' for?
I'm not 'avin' your orts an' slarts.
  —Which on us said you wor?

But I want you to know 'e's not *marryin'* you.
  —Tha wants 'im thy-sèn too bad.
Though I'll see as 'e pays you, an' does what's right.
  —Tha'rt for doin' a lot wi't' lad!

VIII

To think I should 'ave ter 'affle an' caffle
  Wi' a woman, an' name 'er a price
For lettin' me marry the lad as I thought
  Ter marry wi' cabs an' rice!

But we'll go unbeknown ter th' registrar,
  An' give *'er* the money there is;
For I won't be beholden to such as 'er,
  I won't, or my name's not Liz.

IX

Ta'e off thy duty stripes, Tim,
  An' come in 'ere wi' me;
Ta'e off thy p'liceman's helmet
  An' look at me.

I wish tha hadna done it, Tim,
  I do, an' that I do!
For whenever I look thee i' th' face, I s'll see
  Her face too.

I wish I could wesh 'er off'n thee;
  'Appen I can, if I try.
But tha'll ha'e ter promise ter be true ter me
  Till I die. . . .

X

Twenty pounds o' thy own tha hast, an' fifty pound ha'e I;
Thine shall go ter pay the woman, an' wi' my bit we'll buy
All as we s'll want for furniture when tha leaves this place;
An' we'll be married at th' registrar—now lift thy face!

Lift thy face an' look at me, man! canna ter look at me?
Sorry I am for this business, an' sorry if ever I've driven thee
To do such a thing; though it's a poor tale, it is, that I'm bound
    to say,
Afore I can ta'e thee I've got a widder o' forty-five ter pay!

Dunnat thee think but what I've loved thee; I've loved thee too
    well.
An' 'deed an' I wish as this tale o' thine wor niver my tale to
    tell!
Deed an' I wish I c'd 'a' stood at th' altar wi' thee an' bin proud
    o' thee!
That I could 'a' bin first woman ter thee, as tha'rt first man ter
    me!

But we maun ma'e the best of on't. So now rouse up an' look
at me.
Look up an' say tha'rt sorry tha did it; say, tha'rt sorry for me.
They'll turn thee out o' th' force, I doubt me; if they do, we
can see
If my father can get thee a job on t' bank. Say tha'rt sorry,
Timmy!

XI

Ay, I'm sorry, I'm sorry,
But what o' that!
Ay, I'm sorry! Tha nedna worry
Nor fret thy fat.

I'm sorry for thee, I'm sorry f'r 'er,
I'm sorry f'r us a'.
But what then? Tha wants me, does ter
After a'?

Ah'n put my-sèn i' th' wrong, Liz,
An' 'er as well.
An' tha'rt that right, tha knows; 'tis
Other folks in hell.

Tha *art* so sure tha'rt right, Liz!
That damned sure!
But 'ark thee 'ere, that widder woman
's less graspin', if 'er's poor.

What 'er gen, 'er gen me
Beout a thought.

'Er gen me summat; I shanna
  Say it wor nought.

I'm sorry for th' trouble, ay
  As comes on us a'.
But sorry for what I had? why
  I'm not, that's a'.

As for marryin', I shanna marry
  Neither on yer.
Ah've 'ad a' as I can carry
  From you an' from 'er.

So I s'll go an' leave yer,
  Both on yer.
I don't like yer, Liz, I want ter
  Get away from yer.

An' I really like 'er neither,
  Even though I've 'ad
More from 'er than from you; but either
  Of yer's too much for this lad.

Let me go! what's good o' talkin'?
  Let's a' ha' done.
Talk about love o' women!
  Ter me it's no fun.

What bit o' cunt I had wi' 'er
  's all I got out of it.
An' 's not good enough, it isn't
  For a permanent fit.

I'll say good-bye, Liz, to yer,
  Yer too much i' th' right for me.
An' wi' 'er somehow it isn't right.
  So good-bye, an' let's let be!

A WINTER'S TALE

Yesterday the fields were only grey with scattered snow,
And now the longest grass-leaves hardly emerge;
Yet her footsteps mark the snow, and go
On towards the pines at the hill's white verge.

I cannot see her, since the mist's pale scarf
Obscures the dark wood and the dull orange sky;
But she's waiting, I know, impatient and cold, half
Sobs struggling into her frosty sigh.

Why does she come so promptly, when she must know
She's only the nearer to the inevitable farewell?
The hill is steep, on the snow my steps are slow—
Why does she come, when she knows what I have to tell?

SUSPENSE

The wind comes from the north
Blowing little flocks of birds
Like spray across the town,

And a train roaring forth
Rushes stampeding down
South, with flying curds
Of steam, from the darkening north.

Whither I turn and set
Like a needle steadfastly,
Waiting ever to get
The news that she is free;
But ever fixed, as yet,
To the lode of her agony.

THE BRIDE

My love looks like a girl to-night,
  But she is old.
The plaits that lie along her pillow
  Are not gold,
But threaded with filigree silver,
  And uncanny cold.

She looks like a young maiden, since her brow
  Is smooth and fair;
Her cheeks are very smooth, her eyes are closed,
  She sleeps a rare,
Still, winsome sleep, so still, and so composed.

Nay, but she sleeps like a bride, and dreams her dreams
  Of perfect things.
She lies at last, the darling, in the shape of her dream,

And her dead mouth sings
By its shape, like thrushes in clear evenings.

SORROW

Why does the thin grey strand
Floating up from the forgotten
Cigarette between my fingers,
Why does it trouble me?

Ah, you will understand;
When I carried my mother downstairs,
A few times only, at the beginning
Of her soft-foot malady,

I should find, for a reprimand
To my gaiety, a few long grey hairs
On the breast of my coat; and one by one
I watched them float up the dark chimney.

SILENCE

Since I lost you, I am silence-haunted;
Sounds wave their little wings
A moment, then in weariness settle
On the flood that soundless swings.

Whether the people in the street
Like pattering-ripples go by,

Or whether the theatre sighs and sighs
  With a loud, hoarse sigh:

Or the wind shakes a ravel of light
  Over the dead-black river,
Or last night's echoings
  Make the daybreak shiver:

I feel the silence waiting
  To sip them all up again,
In its last completeness drinking
  Down the noise of men.

BROODING GRIEF

A yellow leaf, from the darkness
Hops like a frog before me;
Why should I start and stand still?

I was watching the woman that bore me
Stretched in the brindled darkness
Of the sick-room, rigid with will
To die: and the quick leaf tore me
Back to this rainy swill
Of leaves and lamps and the city street mingled before me.

TROTH WITH THE DEAD

The moon is broken in twain, and half a moon
Beyond me lies on the low, still floor of the sky;

The other half of the broken coin of troth
Is buried away in the dark, where the dead all lie.

They buried her half in the grave when they laid her away;
Pushed gently away and hidden in the thick of her hair
Where it gathered towards the plait, on that very last day;
And like a moon unshowing it must still shine there.

So half lies on the sky, for a general sign
Of the troth with the dead that we are pledged to keep;
Turning its broken edge to the dark, its shine
Ends like a broken love, that turns to the dark of sleep.

And half lies there in the dark where the dead all lie
Lost and yet still connected; and between the two
Strange beams must travel still, for I feel that I
Am lit beneath my heart with a half-moon, weird and blue.

AT A LOOSE END

Many years have I still to burn, detained
Like a candle-flame on this body; but I enclose
Blue shadow within me, a presence which lives contained
In my flame of living, the invisible heart of the rose.

So through these days, while I burn on the fuel of life,
What matter the stuff I lick up in my daily flame;
Seeing the core is a shadow inviolate,
A darkness that dreams my dream for me, ever the same.

RELEASE

Helen, had I known yesterday
That you could discharge the ache
  Out of the wound,
Had I known yesterday that you could take
The turgid electric ache away,
  Drink it up in the ground
Of your soft white body, as lightning
Is drunk from an agonised sky by the earth,
  I should have hated you, Helen.

But since my limbs gushed full of fire,
Since from out of my blood and bone
  Poured a heavy flame
To you, earth of my atmosphere, stone
Of my steel, lovely white flint of desire,
  You have no name.
Earth of my swaying atmosphere,
Substance of my inconstant breath,
  I cannot but cleave to you, Helen.

Since you have drunken up the drear
Death-darkened storm, and death
  Is washed from the blue
Of my eyes, I see you beautiful, and dear.
Beautiful, passive and strong, as the breath
  Of my yearning blows over you.
I see myself as the winds that hover
Half substanceless, and without grave worth.
  But you
  Are the earth I hover over.

UNDER THE OAK

You, if you were sensible,
When I tell you the stars flash signals, each one dreadful,
You would not turn and answer me
"The night is wonderful."

Even you, if you knew
How this darkness soaks me through and through, and infuses
Unholy fear in my essence, you would pause to distinguish
What hurts from what amuses.

For I tell you
Beneath this powerful tree, my whole soul's fluid
Oozes away from me as a sacrifice steam
At the knife of a Druid.

Again I tell you, I bleed, I am bound with withies,
My life runs out.
I tell you my blood runs out on the floor of this oak,
Gout upon gout.

Above me springs the blood-born mistletoe
In the shady smoke.
But who are you, twittering to and fro
Beneath the oak?

What thing better are you, what worse?
What have you to do with the mysteries
Of this ancient place, of my ancient curse?
What place have you in my histories?

PIANO

Softly, in the dusk, a woman is singing to me;
Taking me back down the vista of years, till I see
A child sitting under the piano, in the boom of the tingling strings
And pressing the small, poised feet of a mother who smiles as she sings.

In spite of myself, the insidious mastery of song
Betrays me back, till the heart of me weeps to belong
To the old Sunday evenings at home, with winter outside
And hymns in the cozy parlour, the tinkling piano our guide.

So now it is vain for the singer to burst into clamour
With the great black piano appassionato. The glamour
Of childish days is upon me, my manhood is cast
Down in the flood of remembrance, I weep like a child for the past.

PASSING VISIT TO HELEN

Returning, I find her just the same,
At just the same old delicate game.

Still she says: "Nay, loose no flame
To lick me up and do me harm!
Be all yourself!—for oh, the charm
Of your heart of fire in which I look!
Oh, better there than in any book

Glow and enact the dramas and dreams
I love for ever!—there it seems
You are lovelier than life itself, till desire
Comes licking through the bars of your lips,
And over my face the stray fire slips,
Leaving a burn and an ugly smart
That will have the oil of illusion. Oh, heart
Of fire and beauty, loose no more
Your reptile flames of lust; ah, store
Your passion in the basket of your soul,
Be all yourself, one bonny, burning coal
That stays with steady joy of its own fire!
For in the firing all my porcelain
Of flesh does crackle and shiver and break in pain,
My ivory and marble black with stain,
My veil of sensitive mystery rent in twain,
My altars sullied, I bereft, remain
A priestess execrable, taken in vain—"

So the refrain
Sings itself over, and so the game
Restarts itself wherein I am kept
Like a glowing brazier faintly blue of flame,
So that the delicate love-adept
Can warm her hands and invite her soul,
Sprinkling incense and salt of words
And kisses pale, and sipping the toll
Of incense-smoke that rises like birds.

Yet I've forgotten in playing this game,
Things I have known that shall have no name;
Forgetting the place from which I came

I watch her ward away the flame
Yet warm herself at the fire—then blame
Me that I flicker in the basket;
Me that I glow not with content
To have my substance so subtly spent;
Me that I interrupt her game . . .
I ought to be proud that she should ask it
Of me to be her fire-opal . . .

It is well
Since I am here for so short a spell
Not to interrupt her?—Why should I
Break in by making any reply!

TWENTY YEARS AGO

Round the house were lilacs and strawberries
And foal-foots spangling the paths,
And far away on the sand-hills, dewberries
Caught dust from the sea's long swaths.

Up the wolds the woods were walking,
And nuts fell out of their hair.
At the gate the nets hung, balking
The star-lit rush of a hare.

In the autumn fields, the stubble
Tinkled the music of gleaning.
At a mother's knees, the trouble
Lost all its meaning.

Yea, what good beginnings
  To this sad end!
Have we had our innings?
  God forfend!

SEVEN SEALS

Since this is the last night I keep you home.
Come, I will consecrate you for the journey.

Rather I had you would not go. Nay come,
I will not again reproach you. Lie back
And let me love you a long time ere you go.
For you are sullen-hearted still, and lack
The will to love me. But even so
I will set a seal upon you from my lip,
Will set a guard of honour at each door,
Seal up each channel out of which might slip
Your love for me.

                I kiss your mouth. Ah, love,
Could I but seal its ruddy, shining spring
Of passion, parch it up, destroy, remove
Its softly-stirring crimson welling-up
Of kisses! Oh, help me, God! Here at the source
I'd lie for ever drinking and drawing in
Your fountains, as heaven drinks from out their course
The floods.

            I close your ears with kisses
And seal your nostrils; and round your neck you'll wear—

Nay, let me work—a delicate chain of kisses.
Like beads they go around, and not one misses
To touch its fellow on either side.

And there
Full mid-between the champaign of your breast
I place a great and burning seal of love
Like a dark rose, a mystery of rest
On the slow bubbling of your rhythmic heart.

Nay, I persist, and very faith shall keep
You integral to me. Each door, each mystic port
Of egress from you I will seal and steep
In perfect chrism.

Now it is done. The mort
Will sound in heaven before it is undone.
But let me finish what I have begun
And shirt you now invulnerable in the mail
Of iron kisses, kisses linked like steel.
Put greaves upon your thighs and knees, and frail
Webbing of steel on your feet. So you shall feel
Ensheathed invulnerable with me, with seven
Great seals upon your outgoings, and woven
Chain of my mystic will wrapped perfectly
Upon you, wrapped in indomitable me.

MOONRISE

And who has seen the moon, who has not seen
Her rise from out the chamber of the deep,

Flushed and grand and naked, as from the chamber
Of finished bridegroom, seen her rise and throw
Confession of delight upon the wave,
Littering the waves with her own superscription
Of bliss, till all her lambent beauty shakes toward us
Spread out and known at last, and we are sure
That beauty is a thing beyond the grave,
That perfect, bright experience never falls
To nothingness, and time will dim the moon
Sooner than our full consummation here
In this odd life will tarnish or pass away.

HYMN TO PRIAPUS

My love lies underground
With her face upturned to mine,
And her mouth unclosed in a last long kiss
That ended her life and mine.

I danced at the Christmas party
Under the mistletoe
Along with a ripe, slack country lass
Jostling to and fro.

The big, soft country lass,
Like a loose sheaf of wheat
Slipped through my arms on the threshing floor
At my feet.

The warm, soft country lass,
Sweet as an armful of wheat

At threshing-time broken, was broken
For me, and ah, it was sweet!

Now I am going home
Fulfilled and alone,
I see the great Orion standing
Looking down.

He's the star of my first beloved
Love-making.
The witness of all that bitter-sweet
Heart-aching.

Now he sees this as well,
This last commission.
Nor do I get any look
Of admonition.

He can add the reckoning up
I suppose, between now and then,
Having walked himself in the thorny, difficult
Ways of men.

He has done as I have done
No doubt:
Remembered and forgotten
Turn and about.

My love lies underground
With her face upturned to mine,
And her mouth unclosed in the last long kiss
That ended her life and mine.

She fares in the stark immortal
Fields of death;
I in these goodly, frozen
Fields beneath.

Something in me remembers
And will not forget.
The stream of my life in the darkness
Deathward set!

And something in me has forgotten,
Has ceased to care.
Desire comes up, and contentment
Is debonair.

I, who am worn and careful,
How much do I care?
How is it I grin then, and chuckle
Over despair?

Grief, grief, I suppose and sufficient
Grief makes us free
To be faithless and faithful together
As we have to be.

BEI HENNEF

The little river twittering in the twilight,
The wan, wondering look of the pale sky,
  This is almost bliss.

And everything shut up and gone to sleep,
All the troubles and anxieties and pain
  Gone under the twilight.

Only the twilight now, and the soft "Sh!" of the river
  That will last for ever.

And at last I know my love for you is here;
I can see it all, it is whole like the twilight,
It is large, so large, I could not see it before,
Because of the little lights and flickers and interruptions,
  Troubles, anxieties, and pains.

  You are the call and I am the answer,
  You are the wish, and I the fulfilment,
  You are the night, and I the day.
    What else? it is perfect enough.
    It is perfectly complete,
    You and I,
    What more—?

Strange, how we suffer in spite of this!

Hennef am Rhein

ON THE BALCONY

In front of the sombre mountains, a faint, lost ribbon of rain-
    bow;
And between us and it, the thunder;

And down below in the green wheat, the labourers
Stand like dark stumps, still in the green wheat.

You are near to me, and your naked feet in their sandals,
And through the scent of the balcony's naked timber
I distinguish the scent of your hair; so now the limber
Lightning falls from heaven.

Adown the pale-green glacier river floats
A dark boat through the gloom—and whither?
The thunder roars. But still we have each other!
The naked lightnings in the heaven dither
And disappear—what have we but each other?
The boat has gone.

Icking

A YOUNG WIFE

The pain of loving you
Is almost more than I can bear.

I walk in fear of you.
The darkness starts up where
You stand, and the night comes through
Your eyes when you look at me.

Ah, never before did I see
The shadows that live in the sun!

Now every tall glad tree
Turns round its back to the sun
And looks down on the ground, to see
The shadow it used to shun.

At the foot of each glowing thing
A night lies looking up.

Oh, and I want to sing
And dance, but I can't lift up
My eyes from the shadows: dark
They lie split round the cup.

What is it?—Hark
The faint fine seethe in the air!

Like the seething sound in a shell!
It is death still seething where
The wild-flower shakes its bell
And the skylark twinkles blue—

The pain of loving you
Is almost more than I can bear.

GREEN

The dawn was apple-green,
  The sky was green wine held up in the sun,
The moon was a golden petal between.

She opened her eyes, and green
  They shone, clear like flowers undone
For the first time, now for the first time seen.

Icking

RIVER ROSES

By the Isar, in the twilight
We were wandering and singing,
By the Isar, in the evening
We climbed the huntsman's ladder and sat swinging
In the fir-tree overlooking the marshes,
While river met with river, and the ringing
Of their pale-green glacier water filled the evening.

By the Isar, in the twilight
We found the dark wild roses
Hanging red at the river; and simmering
Frogs were singing, and over the river closes
Was savour of ice and of roses; and glimmering
Fear was abroad. We whispered: "No one knows us.
Let it be as the snake disposes
Here in this simmering marsh."

Kloster Schaeftlarn

GLOIRE DE DIJON

When she rises in the morning
I linger to watch her;

Spreads the bath-cloth underneath the window
And the sunbeams catch her
Glistening white on the shoulders,
While down her sides the mellow
Golden shadow glows as
She stoops to the sponge, and the swung breasts
Sway like full-blown yellow
Gloire de Dijon roses.

She drips herself with water, and the shoulders
Glisten as silver, they crumple up
Like wet and falling roses, and I listen
For the sluicing of their rain-dishevelled petals.
In the window full of sunlight
Concentrates her golden shadow
Fold on fold, until it glows as
Mellow as the glory roses.

Icking

A YOUTH MOWING

There are four men mowing down by the Isar;
I can hear the swish of the scythe-strokes, four
Sharp breaths taken: yea, and I
Am sorry for what's in store.

The first man out of the four that's mowing
Is mine, I claim him once and for all;
Though it's sorry I am, on his young feet, knowing
None of the trouble he's led to stall.

As he sees me bringing the dinner, he lifts
His head as proud as a deer that looks
Shoulder-deep out of the corn; and wipes
His scythe-blade bright, unhooks

The scythe-stone and over the stubble to me.
Lad, thou hast gotten a child in me,
Laddie, a man thou'lt ha'e to be,
Yea, though I'm sorry for thee.

QUITE FORSAKEN

What pain, to wake and miss you!
  To wake with a tightening heart,
And mouth reaching forward to kiss you!

This then at last is the dawn, and the bell
  Clanging at the farm! Such bewilderment
Comes from the sight of the room, I cannot tell.

It is raining. Down the half-obscure road
  Four labourers pass with their scythes
Dejectedly;—a huntsman goes by with his load:

A gun, and a bunched-up deer, its four little feet
  Clustered dead.—And this is the dawn
For which I wanted the night to retreat!

SINNERS

The big mountains sit still in the afternoon light,
  Shadows in their lap;
The bees roll round in the wild-thyme with delight.

We sitting here among the cranberries
  So still in the gap
Of rock, distilling our memories,

Are sinners! Strange! The bee that blunders
  Against me goes off with a laugh.
A squirrel cocks his head on the fence, and wonders

What about sin?—For, it seems
  The mountains have
No shadow of us on their snowy forehead of dreams

As they ought to have. They rise above us
  Dreaming
For ever. One even might think that they love us.

  Little red cranberries cheek to cheek,
  Two great dragon-flies wrestling;
  You, with your forehead nestling
  Against me, and bright peak shining to peak—

There's a love-song for you!—Ah, if only
  There were no teeming
Swarms of mankind in the world, and we were less lonely!

Mayrhofen

DECEMBER NIGHT

Take off your cloak and your hat
And your shoes, and draw up at my hearth
Where never woman sat.

I have made the fire up bright;
Let us leave the rest in the dark
And sit by firelight.

The wine is warm in the hearth;
The flickers come and go.
I will warm your limbs with kisses
Until they glow.

NEW YEAR'S EVE

There are only two things now,
The great black night scooped out
And this fireglow.

This fireglow, the core,
And we the two ripe pips
That are held in store.

Listen, the darkness rings
As it circulates round our fire.
Take off your things.

Your shoulders, your bruised throat!
Your breasts, your nakedness!
This fiery coat!

As the darkness flickers and dips,
As the firelight falls and leaps
From your feet to your lips!

COMING AWAKE

When I woke, the lake-lights were quivering on the wall,
  The sunshine swam in a shoal across and across,
And a hairy, big bee hung over the primulas
  In the window, his body black fur, and the sound of him
    cross.

There was something I ought to remember: and yet
  I did not remember. Why should I? The running lights
And the airy primulas, oblivious
  Of the impending bee—they were fair enough sights.

SPRING MORNING

Ah, through the open door
Is there an almond tree
Aflame with blossom!
  —Let us fight no more.

Among the pink and blue
Of the sky and the almond flowers
A sparrow flutters.
  —We have come through,

It is really spring!—See,
When he thinks himself alone
How he bullies the flowers.
  —Ah, you and me

How happy we'll be!—See him?
He clouts the tufts of flowers
In his impudence.
  —But, did you dream

It would be so bitter? Never mind
It is finished, the spring is here.
And we're going to be summer-happy
  And summer-kind.

We have died, we have slain and been slain,
We are not our old selves any more.
I feel new and eager
  To start again.

It is gorgeous to live and forget.
And to feel quite new.
See the bird in the flowers?—he's making
  A rare to-do!

He thinks the whole blue sky
Is much less than the bit of blue egg
He's got in his nest—we'll be happy,
  You and I, I and you.

With nothing to fight any more—
In each other, at least.

See, how gorgeous the world is
  Outside the door!

HISTORY

The listless beauty of the hour
When snow fell on the apple-trees
And the wood-ash gathered in the fire
And we faced our first miseries.

Then the sweeping sunshine of noon
When the mountains like chariot cars
Were ranked to blue battle—and you and I
Counted our scars.

And then in a strange, grey hour
We lay mouth to mouth, with your face
Under mine like a star on the lake,
And I covered the earth, and all space.

The silent, drifting hours
Of morn after morn
And night drifting up to the night
Yet no pathway worn.

Your life, and mine, my love
Passing on and on, the hate
Fusing closer and closer with love
Till at length they mate.

The Cearne

SONG OF A MAN WHO HAS COME THROUGH

Not I, not I, but the wind that blows through me!
A fine wind is blowing the new direction of Time.
If only I let it bear me, carry me, if only it carry me!
If only I am sensitive, subtle, oh, delicate, a winged gift!
If only, most lovely of all, I yield myself and am borrowed
By the fine, fine wind that takes its course through the chaos
    of the world
Like a fine, an exquisite chisel, a wedge-blade inserted;
If only I am keen and hard like the sheer tip of a wedge
Driven by invisible blows,
The rock will split, we shall come at the wonder, we shall
    find the Hesperides.

Oh, for the wonder that bubbles into my soul,
I would be a good fountain, a good well-head,
Would blur no whisper, spoil no expression.

What is the knocking?
What is the knocking at the door in the night?
It is somebody wants to do us harm.

No, no, it is the three strange angels.
Admit them, admit them.

NEW HEAVEN AND EARTH

I

And so I cross into another world
shyly and in homage linger for an invitation
from this unknown that I would trespass on.

I am very glad, and all alone in the world,
all alone, and very glad, in a new world
where I am disembarked at last.

I could cry with joy, because I am in the new world, just ventured in.
I could cry with joy, and quite freely, there is nobody to know.

And whosoever the unknown people of this unknown world may be
they will never understand my weeping for joy to be adventuring among them
because it will still be a gesture of the old world I am making
which they will not understand, because it is quite, quite foreign to them.

II

I was so weary of the world,
I was so sick of it,
everything was tainted with myself,
skies, trees, flowers, birds, water,

people, houses, streets, vehicles, machines,
nations, armies, war, peace-talking,
work, recreation, governing, anarchy,
it was all tainted with myself, I knew it all to start with
because it was all myself.

When I gathered flowers, I knew it was myself plucking my
own flowering.
When I went in a train, I knew it was myself travelling by
my own invention.
When I heard the cannon of the war, I listened with my own
ears to my own destruction.
When I saw the torn dead, I knew it was my own torn dead
body.
It was all me, I had done it all in my own flesh.

III

I shall never forget the maniacal horror of it all in the end
when everything was me, I knew it all already, I anticipated it
all in my soul
because I was the author and the result
I was the God and the creation at once;
creator, I looked at my creation;
created, I looked at myself, the creator:
it was a maniacal horror in the end.

I was a lover, I kissed the woman I loved,
And God of horror, I was kissing also myself.
I was a father and a begetter of children,

And oh, oh horror, I was begetting and conceiving in my own
body.

IV

At last came death, sufficiency of death,
and that at last relieved me, I died.
I buried my beloved; it was good, I buried myself and was
gone.
War came, and every hand raised to murder;
very good, very good, every hand raised to murder!
Very good, very good, I am a murderer!
It is good, I can murder and murder, and see them fall,
the mutilated, horror-struck youths, a multitude
one on another, and then in clusters together
smashed, all oozing with blood, and burned in heaps
going up in a foetid smoke to get rid of them,
the murdered bodies of youths and men in heaps
the heaps and heaps and horrible reeking heaps
till it is almost enough, till I am reduced perhaps;
thousands and thousands of gaping, hideous foul dead
that are youths and men and me
being burned with oil, and consumed in corrupt thick smoke,
that rolls
and taints and blackens the sky, till at last it is dark, dark as
night, or death, or hell
and I am dead, and trodden to nought in the smoke-sodden
tomb;
dead and trodden to nought in the sour black earth
of the tomb; dead and trodden to nought, trodden to nought.

V

God, but it is good to have died and been trodden out,
trodden to nought in sour, dead earth,
quite to nought,
absolutely to nothing
nothing
nothing
nothing.

For when it is quite, quite nothing, then it is everything.
When I am trodden quite out, quite, quite out,
every vestige gone, then I am here
risen, and setting my foot on another world
risen, accomplishing a resurrection
risen, not born again, but risen, body the same as before,
new beyond knowledge of newness, alive beyond life,
proud beyond inkling or furthest conception of pride,
living where life was never yet dreamed of, nor hinted at,
here, in the other world, still terrestrial
myself, the same as before, yet unaccountably new.

VI

I, in the sour black tomb, trodden to absolute death
I put out my hand in the night, one night, and my hand
touched that which was verily not me,
verily it was not me.
Where I had been was a sudden blaze,
a sudden flaring blaze!

So I put my hand out further, a little further
and I felt that which was not I,
it verily was not I,
it was the unknown.

Ha, I was a blaze leaping up!
I was a tiger bursting into sunlight.
I was greedy, I was mad for the unknown.
I, new-risen, resurrected, starved from the tomb,
starved from a life of devouring always myself,
now here was I, new-awakened, with my hand stretching out
and touching the unknown, the real unknown, the unknown
    unknown.

My God, but I can only say
I touch, I feel the unknown!
I am the first comer!
Cortes, Pisarro, Columbus, Cabot, they are nothing, nothing!
I am the first comer!
I am the discoverer!
I have found the other world!

The unknown, the unknown!
I am thrown upon the shore.
I am covering myself with the sand.
I am filling my mouth with the earth.
I am burrowing my body into the soil.
The unknown, the new world!

VII

It was the flank of my wife
I touched with my hand, I clutched with my hand,
rising, new-awakened from the tomb!
It was the flank of my wife
whom I married years ago
at whose side I have lain for over a thousand nights
and all that previous while, she was I, she was I;
I touched her, it was I who touched and I who was touched.

Yet rising from the tomb, from the black oblivion
stretching out my hand, my hand flung like a drowned man's
    hand on a rock,
I touched her flank and knew I was carried by the current in
    death
over to the new world, and was climbing out on the shore,
risen, not to the old world, the old, changeless I, the old life,
wakened not to the old knowledge
but to a new earth, a new I, a new knowledge, a new world of
    time.

Ah no, I cannot tell you what it is, the new world.
I cannot tell you the mad, astounded rapture of its discovery.
I shall be mad with delight before I have done,
and whosoever comes after will find me in the new world
a madman in rapture.

VIII

Green streams that flow from the innermost continent of the new world,
what are they?
Green and illumined and travelling for ever
dissolved with the mystery of the innermost heart of the continent,
mystery beyond knowledge or endurance, so sumptuous
out of the well-heads of the new world.—

The other, she too has strange green eyes!
White sands and fruits unknown and perfumes that never
can blow across the dark seas to our usual world!
And land that beats with a pulse!
And valleys that draw close in love!
And strange ways where I fall into oblivion of uttermost living!—
Also she who is the other has strange-mounded breasts and strange sheer slopes, and white levels.

Sightless and strong oblivion in utter life takes possession of me!
The unknown, strong current of life supreme
drowns me and sweeps me away and holds me down
to the sources of mystery, in the depths,
extinguishes there my risen resurrected life
and kindles it further at the core of utter mystery.

Greatham

POMEGRANATE

You tell me I am wrong.
Who are you, who is anybody to tell me I am wrong?
I am not wrong.

In Syracuse, rock left bare by the viciousness of Greek women,
No doubt you have forgotten the pomegranate trees in flower,
Oh so red, and such a lot of them.

Whereas at Venice,
Abhorrent, green, slippery city
Whose Doges were old, and had ancient eyes,
In the dense foliage of the inner garden
Pomegranates like bright green stone,
And barbed, barbed with a crown.
Oh, crown of spiked green metal
Actually growing!

Now is Tuscany,
Pomegranates to warm your hands at;
And crowns, kingly, generous, tilting crowns
Over the left eyebrow.

And, if you dare, the fissure!

Do you mean to tell me you will see no fissure?
Do you prefer to look on the plain side?

For all that, the setting suns are open.
The end cracks open with the beginning:
Rosy, tender, glittering within the fissure.

Do you mean to tell me there should be no fissure?
No glittering, compact drops of dawn?
Do you mean it is wrong, the gold-filmed skin, integument, shown ruptured?

For my part, I prefer my heart to be broken.
It is so lovely, dawn-kaleidoscopic within the crack.

San Gervasio in Tuscany

ST. MARK

There was a lion in Judah
Which whelped, and was Mark.

But winged.
A lion with wings.
At least at Venice.
Even as late as Daniele Manin.

Why should he have wings?
Is he to be a bird also?
Or a spirit?
Or a winged thought?
Or a soaring consciousness?

Evidently he is all that,
The lion of the spirit.

Ah, Lamb of God,
Would a wingless lion lie down before Thee, as this winged
lion lies?

The lion of the spirit.

Once he lay in the mouth of a cave
And sunned his whiskers,
And lashed his tail slowly, slowly
Thinking of voluptuousness
Even of blood.

But later, in the sun of the afternoon,
Having tasted all there was to taste, and having slept his fill
He fell to frowning, as he lay with his head on his paws
And the sun coming in through the narrowest fibril of a slit
in his eyes.

So, nine-tenths asleep, motionless, bored, and statically angry,
He saw in a shaft of light a lamb on a pinnacle, balancing a
flag on its paw,
And he was thoroughly startled.

Going out to investigate
He found the lamb beyond him, on the inaccessible pinnacle
of light.
So he put his paw to his nose, and pondered.

"Guard my sheep," came the silvery voice from the pinnacle,
"And I will give thee the wings of the morning."
So the lion of the senses thought it was worth it.

Hence he became a curly sheep-dog with dangerous propensities,
As Carpaccio will tell you:
Ramping round, guarding the flock of mankind,
Sharpening his teeth on the wolves,
Ramping up through the air like a kestrel
And lashing his tail above the world
And enjoying the sensation of heaven and righteousness and voluptuous wrath.

There is a new sweetness in his voluptuously licking his paw
Now that it is a weapon of heaven.
There is a new ecstasy in his roar of desirous love
Now that it sounds self-conscious through the unlimited sky.
He is well aware of himself
And he cherishes voluptuous delights, and thinks about them
And ceases to be a blood-thirsty king of beasts
And becomes the faithful sheep-dog of the Shepherd, thinking of his voluptuous pleasures of chasing the sheep to the fold
And increasing the flock, and perhaps giving a real nip here and there, a real pinch, but always well meant.

And somewhere there is a lioness,
The she-mate.
Whelps play between the paws of the lion,
And she-mate purrs,
Their castle is impregnable, their cave,
The sun comes in their lair, they are well-off,
A well-to-do family.

Then the proud lion stalks abroad alone,
And roars to announce himself to the wolves

And also to encourage the red-cross Lamb
And also to insure a goodly increase in the world.

Look at him, with his paw on the world
At Venice and elsewhere.
Going blind at last.

FISH

Fish, oh Fish,
So little matters!

Whether the waters rise and cover the earth
Or whether the waters wilt in the hollow places,
All one to you.

Aqueous, subaqueous,
Submerged
And wave-thrilled.

As the waters roll
Roll you.
The waters wash,
You wash in oneness
And never emerge.

Never know,
Never grasp.

Your life a sluice of sensation along your sides,
A flush at the flails of your fins, down the whorl of your tail,

And water wetly on fire in the grates of your gills;
Fixed water-eyes.

Even snakes lie together.

But oh, fish, that rock in water,
You lie only with the waters;
One touch.

No fingers, no hands and feet, no lips;
No tender muzzles,
No wistful bellies,
No loins of desire,
None.

You and the naked element,
Sway-wave.
Curvetting bits of tin in the evening light.

Who is it ejects his sperm to the naked flood?
In the wave-mother?
Who swims enwombed?
Who lies with the waters of his silent passion, womb-element?
—Fish in the waters under the earth.

What price *his* bread upon the waters?

Himself all silvery himself
In the element,
No more.

Nothing more.

Himself,
And the element.
Food, of course!
Water-eager eyes,
Mouth-gate open
And strong spine urging, driving;
And desirous belly gulping.

Fear also!
He knows fear!
Water-eyes craning,
A rush that almost screams,
Almost fish-voice
As the pike comes . . .
Then gay fear, that turns the tail sprightly, from a shadow.

Food, and fear, and joie de vivre,
Without love.

The other way about:
Joie de vivre, and fear and food,
All without love.

Quelle joie de vivre
Dans l'eau!
Slowly to gape through the waters,
Alone with the element;
To sink, and rise, and go to sleep with the waters;
To speak endless inaudible wavelets into the wave;
To breathe from the flood at the gills,
Fish-blood slowly running next to the flood, extracting fish-
    fire;

To have the element under one, like a lover;
And to spring away with a curvetting click in the air,
Provocative.
Dropping back with a slap on the face of the flood.
And merging oneself!

To be a fish!

So utterly without misgiving
To be a fish
In the waters.

Loveless, and so lively!
Born before God was love,
Or life knew loving.
Beautifully beforehand with it all.
Admitted, they swarm in companies,
Fishes.
They drive in shoals.
But soundless, and out of contact.
They exchange no word, no spasm, not even anger.
Not one touch.
Many suspended together, forever apart,
Each one alone with the waters, upon one wave with the rest.

A magnetism in the water between them only.

I saw a water serpent swim across the Anapo,
And I said to my heart, *look, look at him!*
With his head up, steering like a bird!
He's a rare one, but he belongs . . .

But sitting in a boat on the Zeiler lake
And watching the fishes in the breathing waters
Lift and swim and go their way—

I said to my heart, *who are these?*
And my heart couldn't own them . . .

A slim young pike, with smart fins
And a grey-striped suit, a young cub of a pike
Slouching along away below, half out of sight,
Like a lout on an obscure pavement . . .

Aha, there's somebody in the know!

But watching closer
That motionless deadly motion,
That unnatural barrel body, that long ghoul nose . . .
I left off hailing him.

I had made a mistake, I didn't know him,
This grey, monotonous soul in the water,
This intense individual in shadow,
Fish-alive.

I didn't know his God,
I didn't know his God.

Which is perhaps the last admission that life has to wring out
of us.

I saw, dimly,
Once a big pike rush,

And small fish fly like splinters.
And I said to my heart, *there are limits*
To you, my heart;
And to the one God.
Fish are beyond me.

Other Gods
Beyond my range . . . gods beyond my God . . .

They are beyond me, are fishes.
I stand at the pale of my being
And look beyond, and see
Fish, in the outerwards,
As one stands on a bank and looks in.

I have waited with a long rod
And suddenly pulled a gold-and-greenish, lucent fish from below,
And had him fly like a halo round my head,
Lunging in the air on the line.

Unhooked his gorping, water-horny mouth,
And seen his horror-tilted eye,
His red-gold, water-precious, mirror-flat bright eye;
And felt him beat in my hand, with his mucous, leaping life-throb.

And my heart accused itself
Thinking: *I am not the measure of creation.*
This is beyond me, this fish.
His God stands outside my God.

And the gold-and-green pure lacquer-mucous comes off in
  my hand,
And the red-gold mirror-eye stares and dies,
And the water-suave contour dims.

But not before I have had to know
He was born in front of my sunrise,
Before my day.

He outstarts me.
And I, a many-fingered horror of daylight to him,
Have made him die.

Fishes
With their gold, red eyes, and green-pure gleam, and under-
  gold,
And their pre-world loneliness,
And more-than-lovelessness,
And white meat;
They move in other circles.

Outsiders.
Water-wayfarers.
Things of one element.
Aqueous,
Each by itself.

Cats, and the Neapolitans,
Sulphur sun-beasts,
Thirst for fish as for more-than-water;
Water-alive
To quench their over-sulphurous lusts.

But I, I only wonder
And don't know.
I don't know fishes.

In the beginning
Jesus was called The Fish . . .
And in the end.

Zell-am-See

BAT

At evening, sitting on this terrace,
When the sun from the west, beyond Pisa, beyond the mountains of Carrara
Departs, and the world is taken by surprise . . .

When the tired flower of Florence is in gloom beneath the glowing
Brown hills surrounding . . .

When under the arches of the Ponte Vecchio
A green light enters against the stream, flush from the west,
Against the current of obscure Arno . . .

Look up, and you see things flying
Between the day and the night;
Swallows with spools of dark thread sewing the shadows together.

A circle swoop, and a quick parabola under the bridge arches
Where light pushes through;
A sudden turning upon itself of a thing in the air.
A dip to the water.

And you think:
"The swallows are flying so late!"

Swallows?

Dark air-life looping
Yet missing the pure loop . . .
A twitch, a twitter, an elastic shudder in flight
And serrated wings against the sky,
Like a glove, a black glove thrown up at the light,
And falling back.

Never swallows!
Bats!
The swallows are gone.

At a wavering instant the swallows give way to bats
By the Ponte Vecchio . . .
Changing guard.

Bats, and an uneasy creeping in one's scalp
As the bats swoop overhead!
Flying madly.

Pipistrello!
Black piper on an infinitesimal pipe.
Little lumps that fly in air and have voices indefinite, wildly
vindictive;

Wings like bits of umbrella.

Bats!

Creatures that hang themselves up like an old rag to sleep;
And disgustingly upside down.
Hanging upside down like rows of disgusting old rags
And grinning in their sleep.
Bats!

In China the bat is a symbol of happiness.

Not for me!

SNAKE

A snake came to my water-trough
On a hot, hot day, and I in pyjamas for the heat,
To drink there.

In the deep, strange-scented shade of the great dark carob
tree
I came down the steps with my pitcher
And must wait, must stand and wait, for there he was at the
trough before me.

He reached down from a fissure in the earth-wall in the gloom
And trailed his yellow-brown slackness soft-bellied down,
over the edge of the stone trough

And rested his throat upon the stone bottom,
And where the water had dripped from the tap, in a small
clearness,
He sipped with his straight mouth,
Softly drank through his straight gums, into his slack long
body,
Silently.

Someone was before me at my water-trough,
And I, like a second comer, waiting.

He lifted his head from his drinking, as cattle do,
And looked at me vaguely, as drinking cattle do,
And flickered his two-forked tongue from his lips, and mused
a moment,
And stooped and drank a little more,
Being earth-brown, earth-golden from the burning bowels of
the earth
On the day of Sicilian July, with Etna smoking.

The voice of my education said to me
He must be killed,
For in Sicily the black, black snakes are innocent, the gold are
venomous.

And voices in me said, If you were a man
You would take a stick and break him now, and finish him off.

But must I confess how I liked him,
How glad I was he had come like a guest in quiet, to drink at
my water-trough
And depart peaceful, pacified, and thankless,
Into the burning bowels of this earth?

Was it cowardice, that I dared not kill him?
Was it perversity, that I longed to talk to him?
Was it humility, to feel so honoured?
I felt so honoured.

And yet those voices:
If you were not afraid, you would kill him!

And truly I was afraid, I was most afraid,
But even so, honoured still more
That he should seek my hospitality
From out the dark door of the secret earth.

He drank enough
And lifted his head, dreamily, as one who has drunken,
And flickered his tongue like a forked night on the air, so
black,
Seeming to lick his lips,
And looked around like a god, unseeing, into the air,
And slowly turned his head,
And slowly, very slowly, as if thrice adream,
Proceeded to draw his slow length curving round
And climb again the broken bank of my wall-face.

And as he put his head into that dreadful hole,
And as he slowly drew up, snake-easing his shoulders, and
entered farther,
A sort of horror, a sort of protest against his withdrawing into
that horrid black hole,
Deliberately going into the blackness, and slowly drawing
himself after,
Overcame me now his back was turned.

I looked around, I put down my pitcher,
I picked up a clumsy log
And threw it at the water-trough with a clatter.

I think I did not hit him,
But suddenly that part of him that was left behind convulsed
in undignified haste,
Writhed like lightning, and was gone
Into the black hole, the earth-lipped fissure in the wall-front,
At which, in the intense still noon, I stared with fascination.

And immediately I regretted it.
I thought how paltry, how vulgar, what a mean act!
I despised myself and the voices of my accursed human education.

And I thought of the albatross,
And I wished he would come back, my snake.

For he seemed to me again like a king,
Like a king in exile, uncrowned in the underworld,
Now due to be crowned again.

And so, I missed my chance with one of the lords
Of life.
And I have something to expiate;
A pettiness.

Taormina

TORTOISE GALLANTRY

Making his advances
He does not look at her, nor sniff at her,
No, not even sniff at her, his nose is blank.

Only he senses the vulnerable folds of skin
That work beneath her while she sprawls along
In her ungainly pace,
Her folds of skin that work and row
Beneath the earth-soiled hovel in which she moves.

And so he strains beneath her housey walls
And catches her trouser-legs in his beak
Suddenly, or her skinny limb,
And strange and grimly drags her
Like a dog,
Only agelessly silent, with a reptile's awful persistency.

Grim, gruesome gallantry, to which he is doomed.
Dragged out of an eternity of silent isolation
And doomed to partiality, partial being,
Ache, and want of being,
Want,
Self-exposure, hard humiliation, need to add himself on to her.

Born to walk alone,
Fore-runner,
Now suddenly distracted into this mazy side-track,
This awkward, harrowing pursuit,
This grim necessity from within.

Does she know
As she moves eternally slowly away?
Or is he driven against her with a bang, like a bird flying in
the dark against a window,
All knowledgeless?

The awful concussion,
And the still more awful need to persist, to follow, follow,
continue,
Driven, after aeons of pristine, for-god-like singleness and
oneness,
At the end of some mysterious, red-hot iron,
Driven away from himself into her tracks,
Forced to crash against her.

Stiff, gallant, irascible, crook-legged reptile,
Little gentleman,
Sorry plight,
We ought to look the other way.

Save that, having come with you so far,
We will go on to the end.

HUMMING-BIRD

I can imagine, in some otherworld
Primeval-dumb, far back
In that most awful stillness, that only gasped and hummed,
Humming-birds raced down the avenues.

Before anything had a soul,
While life was a heave of Matter, half inanimate,
This little bit chipped off in brilliance
And went whizzing through the slow, vast, succulent stems.

I believe there were no flowers then,
In the world where the humming-bird flashed ahead of creation.
I believe he pierced the slow vegetable veins with his long beak.

Probably he was big
As mosses, and little lizards, they say, were once big.
Probably he was a jabbing, terrifying monster.

We look at him through the wrong end of the telescope of Time,
Luckily for us.

Española

YOU

You, you don't know me.
When have your knees ever nipped me
like fire-tongs a live coal
for a minute?

HOW BEASTLY THE BOURGEOIS IS

How beastly the bourgeois is
especially the male of the species—

Presentable, eminently presentable—
shall I make you a present of him?

Isn't he handsome? isn't he healthy? isn't he a fine specimen?
doesn't he look the fresh clean englishman, outside?
Isn't it god's own image? tramping his thirty miles a day
after partridges, or a little rubber ball?
wouldn't you like to be like that, well off, and quite the thing?

Oh, but wait!
Let him meet a new emotion, let him be faced with another
    man's need,
let him come home to a bit of moral difficulty, let life face
    him with a new demand on his understanding
and then watch him go soggy, like a wet meringue.
Watch him turn into a mess, either a fool or a bully.
Just watch the display of him, confronted with a new demand
    on his intelligence,
a new life-demand.

How beastly the bourgeois is
especially the male of the species—

Nicely groomed, like a mushroom
standing there so sleek and erect and eyeable—
and like a fungus, living on the remains of bygone life
sucking his life out of the dead leaves of greater life than his
    own.

And even so, he's stale, he's been there too long.
Touch him, and you'll find he's all gone inside
just like an old mushroom, all wormy inside, and hollow
under a smooth skin and an upright appearance.

Full of seething, wormy, hollow feelings
rather nasty—
How beastly the bourgeois is!

Standing in their thousands, these appearances, in damp England
what a pity they can't all be kicked over
like sickening toadstools, and left to melt back, swiftly
into the soil of England.

TO BE SUPERIOR

How nice it is to be superior!
Because really, it's no use pretending, one *is* superior, isn't one?
I mean people like you and me.—

Quite! I quite agree.
The trouble is, everybody thinks they're just as superior
as we are; just as superior.—

That's what's so boring! people are so boring.
But they can't really think it, do you think?
At the bottom, they must *know* we are really superior
don't you think?
don't you think, *really*, they *know* we're their superiors?—

I couldn't say.
I've never got to the bottom of superiority.
I should like to.

SWAN

Far-off
at the core of space
at the quick
of time
beats
and goes still
the great swan upon the waters of all endings
the swan within vast chaos, within the electron.

For us
no longer he swims calmly
nor clacks across the forces furrowing a great gay trail
of happy energy,
nor is he nesting passive upon the atoms,
nor flying north desolative icewards
to the sleep of ice,
nor feeding in the marshes,
nor honking horn-like into the twilight.—

But he stoops, now
in the dark
upon us;
he is treading our women
and we men are put out

as the vast white bird
furrows our fatherless women
with unknown shocks
and stamps his black marsh-feet on their white and marshy
flesh.

WE ARE TRANSMITTERS

As we live, we are transmitters of life.
And when we fail to transmit life, life fails to flow through us.

That is part of the mystery of sex, it is a flow onwards.
Sexless people transmit nothing.

And if, as we work, we can transmit life into our work,
life, still more life, rushes into us to compensate, to be ready
and we ripple with life through the days.

Even if it is a woman making an apple dumpling, or a man a
stool,
if life goes into the pudding, good is the pudding,
good is the stool,
content is the woman, with fresh life rippling in to her,
content is the man.

Give, and it shall be given unto you
is still the truth about life.
But giving life is not so easy.
It doesn't mean handing it out to some mean fool, or letting
the living dead eat you up.
It means kindling the life-quality where it was not,

even if it's only in the whiteness of a washed pocket-
handkerchief.

NOVEMBER BY THE SEA

Now in November nearer comes the sun
down the abandoned heaven.

As the dark closes round him, he draws nearer
as if for our company.

At the base of the lower brain
the sun in me declines to his winter solstice
and darts a few gold rays
back to the old year's sun across the sea.

A few gold rays thickening down to red
as the sun of my soul is setting
setting fierce and undaunted, wintry
but setting, setting behind the sounding sea between my ribs,

The wide sea wins, and the dark
winter, and the great day-sun, and the sun in my soul
sinks, sinks to setting and the winter solstice
downward, they race in decline
my sun, and the great gold sun.

THE ELEPHANT IS SLOW TO MATE

The elephant, the huge old beast,
    is slow to mate;
he finds a female, they show no haste,
    they wait

for the sympathy in their vast shy hearts
    slowly, slowly to rouse
as they loiter along the river-beds
    and drink and browse

and dash in panic through the brake
    of forest with the herd,
and sleep in massive silence, and wake
    together, without a word.

So slowly the great hot elephant hearts
    grow full of desire,
and the great beasts mate in secret at last,
    hiding their fire.

Oldest they are and the wisest of beasts
    so they know at last
how to wait for the loneliest of feasts,
    for the full repast.

They do not snatch, they do not tear;
    their massive blood
moves as the moon-tides, near, more near,
    till they touch in flood.

LITTLE FISH

The tiny fish enjoy themselves
in the sea.
Quick little splinters of life,
their little lives are fun to them
in the sea.

THE MOSQUITO KNOWS

The mosquito knows full well, small as he is
he's a beast of prey.
But after all
he only takes his bellyful,
he doesn't put my blood in the bank.

SELF-PITY

I never saw a wild thing
sorry for itself.
A small bird will drop frozen dead from a bough
without ever having felt sorry for itself.

SICK

I am sick, because I have given myself away.
I have given myself to the people when they came

so cultured, even bringing little gifts,
so they pecked a shred of my life, and flew off with a croak
of sneaking exultance.
So now I have lost too much, and am sick.

I am trying now to learn never
to give of my life to the dead,
never, not the tiniest shred.

BEAUTIFUL OLD AGE

It ought to be lovely to be old
to be full of the peace that comes of experience
and wrinkled ripe fulfilment.

The wrinkled smile of completeness that follows a life
lived undaunted and unsoured with accepted lies.
If people lived without accepting lies
they would ripen like apples, and be scented like pippins
in their old age.

Soothing, old people should be, like apples
when one is tired of love.
Fragrant like yellowing leaves, and dim with the soft
stillness and satisfaction of autumn.

And a girl should say:
It must be wonderful to live and grow old.
Look at my mother, how rich and still she is!—

And a young man should think: By Jove
my father has faced all weathers, but it's been a life!—

WHEN THE RIPE FRUIT FALLS

When the ripe fruit falls
its sweetness distils and trickles away into the veins of the
earth.

When fulfilled people die
the essential oil of their experience enters
the veins of living space, and adds a glisten
to the atom, to the body of immortal chaos.

For space is alive
and it stirs like a swan
whose feathers glisten
silky with oil of distilled experience.

FIRE

Fire is dearer to us than love or food,
hot, hurrying, yet it burns if you touch it.

What we ought to do
is not to add our love together, or our good-will, or any of
that,
for we're sure to bring in a lot of lies,

but our fire, our elemental fire
so that it rushes up in a huge blaze like a phallus into hollow
space
and fecundates the zenith and the nadir
and sends off millions of sparks of new atoms
and singes us, and burns the house down.

I WISH I KNEW A WOMAN

I wish I knew a woman
who was like a red fire on the hearth
glowing after the day's restless draughts.

So that one could draw near her
in the red stillness of the dusk
and really take delight in her
without having to make the polite effort of loving her
or the mental effort of making her acquaintance.
Without having to take a chill, talking to her.

LATTER-DAY SINNERS

The worst of the younger generation, those Latter-Day sinners,
is that they calmly assert: We only thrill to perversity, murder, suicide, rape—
Bragging a little, really,

and at the same time, expect to go on calmly eating good dinners for the next fifty years.

They say: *Après moi le déluge!* and calmly expect
that the deluge will never be turned on them, only *after* them.

Post me, nihil!— But perhaps, my dears,
nihil will come along and hit you on the head.

Why should the deluge wait while these young gentry go on eating
good dinners for fifty more long years?
Why should our Latter-Day sinners expect such a long smooth run
for their very paltry little bit of money?
If you are expecting a Second Advent in the shape of a deluge
you mustn't expect it also to wait for your convenience.

WILLY WET-LEG

I can't stand Willy wet-leg,
can't stand him at any price.
He's resigned, and when you hit him
he lets you hit him twice.

IMAGE-MAKING LOVE

And now
the best of all
is to be alone, to possess one's soul in silence.

Nakedly to be alone, unseen
is better than anything else in the world,
a relief like death.

Always
at the core of me
burns the small flame of anger, gnawing
from trespassed contacts, from red-hot finger bruises, on my
    inward flesh.

Always
in the eyes of those who loved me
I have seen at last the image of him they loved
and took for me
mistook for me.

And always
it was a simulacrum, something
like me, and like a gibe at me.

So now I want, above all things
to preserve my nakedness
from the gibe of image-making love.

ANDRAITX — POMEGRANATE FLOWERS

It is June, it is June
the pomegranates are in flower,
the peasants are bending cutting the bearded wheat.

The pomegranates are in flower
beside the high road, past the deathly dust,
and even the sea is silent in the sun.

Short gasps of flame in the green of night, way off
the pomegranates are in flower,
small sharp red flowers in the night of leaves.

And noon is suddenly dark, is lustrous, is silent and dark
men are unseen, beneath the shading hats;
only, from out the foliage of the secret loins
red flamelets here and there reveal
a man, a woman there.

HEALING

I am not a mechanism, an assembly of various sections.
And it is not because the mechanism is working wrongly,
that I am ill.
I am ill because of wounds to the soul, to the deep emotional
self
and the wounds to the soul take a long, long time, only time
can help
and patience, and a certain difficult repentance
long, difficult repentance, realisation of life's mistake, and the
freeing oneself
from the endless repetition of the mistake
which mankind at large has chosen to sanctify.

CITY LIFE

When I am in a great city, I know that I despair.
I know there is no hope for us, death waits, it is useless to care.

For oh the poor people, that are flesh of my flesh,
I, that am flesh of their flesh,
when I see the iron hooked into their faces
their poor, their fearful faces
I scream in my soul, for I know I cannot
take the iron hooks out of their faces, that make them so
drawn,
nor cut the invisible wires of steel that pull them
back and forth, to work, back and forth to work,
like fearful and corpse-like fishes hooked and being played
by some malignant fisherman on an unseen shore
where he does not choose to land them yet, hooked fishes of
the factory world.

TREES IN THE GARDEN

Ah in the thunder air
how still the trees are!

And the lime tree, lovely and tall, every leaf silent
hardly looses even a last breath of perfume.

And the ghostly, creamy coloured little tree of leaves
white, ivory white among the rambling greens,

how evanescent, variegated elder, she hesitates on the green
grass
as if, in another moment, she would disappear
with all her grace of foam!

And the larch that is only a column, it goes up too tall to see:
and the balsam pines that are blue with the grey-blue blueness
of things from the sea,
and the young copper beech, its leaves red-rosy at the ends,
how still they are together, they stand so still
in the thunder air, all strangers to one another
as the green grass glows upwards, strangers in the garden.

THE GODS! THE GODS!

People were bathing, and posturing themselves on the beach
and all was dreary, great robot limbs, robot breasts
robot voices, robot even the gay umbrellas.

But a woman, shy and alone, was washing herself under a tap
and the glimmer of the presence of the gods was like lilies,
and like water-lilies.

THE DEEPEST SENSUALITY

The profoundest of all sensualities
is the sense of truth
and the next deepest sensual experience
is the sense of justice.

NOTHING TO SAVE

There is nothing to save, now all is lost,
but a tiny core of stillness in the heart
like the eye of a violet.

THE ENGLISH ARE SO NICE!

The English are so nice
so awfully nice
they are the nicest people in the world.

And what's more, they're very nice about being nice
about your being nice as well!
If you're not nice they soon make you feel it.

Americans and French and Germans and so on
they're all very well
but they're not *really* nice, you know.
They're not nice in *our* sense of the word, are they now?

That's why one doesn't have to take them seriously.
We must be nice to them, of course,
of course, naturally.
But it doesn't really matter what you say to them,
they don't really understand
you can just say anything to them:
be nice, you know, just nice
but you must never take them seriously, they wouldn't under-
    stand,

just be nice, you know! oh, fairly nice,
not too nice of course, they take advantage
but nice enough, just nice enough
to let them feel they're not quite as nice as they might be.

SEARCH FOR LOVE

Those that go searching for love
only make manifest their own lovelessness,
and the loveless never find love,
only the loving find love,
and they never have to seek for it.

TERRA INCOGNITA

There are vast realms of consciousness still undreamed of
vast ranges of experience, like the humming of unseen harps.
we know nothing of, within us.

Oh when man escaped from the barbed-wire entanglement
of his own ideas and his own mechanical devices
there is a marvellous rich world of contact and sheer fluid
    beauty
and fearless face-to-face awareness of now-naked life
and me, and you, and other men and women
and grapes, and ghouls, and ghosts and green moonlight
and ruddy-orange limbs stirring the limbo
of the unknown air, and eyes so soft

softer than the space between the stars.
And all things, and nothing, and being and not-being
alternately palpitant,
when at last we escape the barbed-wire enclosure
of *Know Thyself*, knowing we can never know,
we can but touch, and wonder, and ponder, and make our
effort
and dangle in a last fastidious fine delight
as the fuchsia does, dangling her reckless drop
of purple after so much putting forth
and slow mounting marvel of a little tree.

THOMAS EARP

I heard a little chicken chirp:
My name is Thomas, Thomas Earp!
And I can neither paint nor write
I only can set other people right.

All people that can write or paint
do tremble under my complaint.
For I am a chicken, and I can chirp,
and my name is Thomas, Thomas Earp.

PUSS-PUSS!

—Oh, Auntie, isn't he a beauty! And is he a gentleman or a
lady?

—Neither, my dear! I had him fixed. It saves him from so many undesirable associations.

LONDON MERCURY

Oh, when Mercury came to London
they had him "fixed."
It saves him from so many undesirable associations.

And now all the Aunties like him so much,
because, you see, he is "neither, my dear!"

THE WHITE HORSE

The youth walks up to the white horse, to put its halter on
and the horse looks at him in silence.
They are so silent they are in another world.

PRAYER

Give me the moon at my feet
Put my feet upon the crescent, like a Lord!
O let my ankles be bathed in moonlight, that I may go
sure and moon-shod, cool and bright-footed
towards my goal

For the sun is hostile, now
his face is like the red lion,

. . . .

LORDS OF THE DAY AND NIGHT

Lo! I am always here!
Far in the hollow of space
I brush the wing of the day
And put light on your face.
The other wing brushes the dark
But I, I am always in place.

Yea, I am always here. I am Lord
In every way. And the lords among men
See me through the flashing of wings.
They see me and loose me again.
But lo! I am always here
Within ken.

The multitude see me not.
They see only the waving of wings,
The coming and going of things.
The cold and the hot.

But ye that perceive me between
The tremors of night and the day,
I make you the Lords of the Way
Unseen.

The path between gulfs of the dark and the steeps of the light;
The path like a snake that is gone, like the length of a fuse to
ignite
The substance of shadow, that bursts and explodes into sight.

I am here undeparting. I sit tight
Between the wings of the endless flight,
At the depths of the peace and the fight.

Deep in the moistures of peace,
And far down the muzzle of the fight
You shall find me, who am neither increase
Nor destruction, different quite.

I am far beyond
The horizons of love and strife.
Like a star, like a pond
That washes the lords of life.

QUETZALCOATL LOOKS DOWN ON MEXICO

Jesus had gone far up the dark slope, when he looked back.
Quetzalcoatl, my brother, he called. Send me my images,
And the images of my mother, and the images of my saints.
Send me them by the swift way, the way of the sparks,
That I may hold them like memories in my arms when I go to
sleep.

And Quetzalcoatl called back: I will do it.

Then he laughed, seeing the sun dart fiercely at him.
He put up his hand, and held back the sun with his shadow.

So he passed the yellow one, who lashed like a dragon in vain.
And having passed the yellow one, he saw the earth beneath.
And he saw Mexico lying like a dark woman with white breast-tips.

Wondering he stepped nearer, and looked at her,
At her trains, at her railways and her automobiles,
At her cities of stone and her huts of straw.
And he said: Surely this looks very curious!

He sat within the hollow of a cloud, and saw the men that worked in the fields, with foreign overseers.
He saw the men that were blind, reeling with aguardiente.
He saw the women that were not clean.
He saw the hearts of them all, that were black, and heavy, with a stone of anger at the bottom.

Surely, he said, this is a curious people I have found!

So leaning forward on his cloud, he said to himself:
I will call to them.

Holá! Holá! Mexicanos! Glance away a moment towards me.
Just turn your eyes this way, Mexicanos!

They turned not at all, they glanced not one his way.

Holálá! Mexicanos! Holálá!
They have gone stone deaf! he said.

So he blew down on them, to blow his breath in their faces.
But in the weight of their stupefaction, none of them knew.

Holálá! What a pretty people!
All gone stupefied!

A falling star was running like a white dog over a plain.
He whistled to it loudly, twice, till it fell to his hand.
In his hand it lay and went dark.
It was the Stone of Change.

This is the stone of change! he said.

So he tossed it awhile in his hand, and played with it.
Then suddenly he spied the old lake, and he threw it in.
It fell in.
And two men looked up.

Holálá! he said. *Mexicanos!*
Are there two of you awake?
So he laughed, and one heard him laughing.

Why are you laughing? asked the first man of Quetzalcoatl.

I hear the voice of my First Man ask me why I am laughing?
Holálá Mexicanos! It is funny!
To see them so glum and so lumpish!

Hey! First Man of my name! Hark here!
Here is my sign.
Get a place ready for me.

Send Jesus his images back, Mary and the saints and all.
Wash yourself, and rub oil in your skin.
On the seventh day, let every man wash himself, and put oil on his skin; let every woman.
Let him have no animal walk on his body, nor through the shadow of his hair. Say the same to the women.
Tell them they all are fools, that I'm laughing at them.
The first thing I did when I saw them, was to laugh at the sight of such fools.
Such lumps, such frogs with stones in their bellies.
Tell them they are like frogs with stones in their bellies, can't hop!
Tell them they must get the stones out of their bellies,
Get rid of their heaviness,
Their lumpishness,
Or I'll smother them all.
I'll shake the earth, and swallow them up, with their cities.
I'll send fire and ashes upon them, and smother them all.
I'll turn their blood like sour milk rotten with thunder,
They will bleed rotten blood, in pestilence.
Even their bones shall crumble.

Tell them so, First Man of my Name.

For the sun and the moon are alive, and watching with gleaming eyes.
And the earth is alive, and ready to shake off his fleas.
And the stars are ready with stones to throw in the faces of men.
And the air that blows good breath in the nostrils of people and beasts
Is ready to blow bad breath upon them, to perish them all.

The stars and the earth and the sun and the moon and the winds
Are about to dance the war dance round you, men!
When I say the word, they will start.
For suns and stars and earth and the very rains are weary
Of tossing and rolling the substance of life to your lips.
They are saying to one another: Let us make an end
Of those ill-smelling tribes of men, these frogs that can't jump,
These cocks that can't crow
These pigs that can't grunt
This flesh that smells
These words that are all flat
These money vermin.
These white men, and red men, and yellow men, and brown men, and black men
That are neither white, nor red, nor yellow, nor brown, nor black
But everyone of them dirtyish.
Let us have a spring cleaning in the world.
For men upon the body of the earth are like lice,
Devouring the earth into sores.
This is what stars and sun and earth and moon and winds and rain
Are discussing with one another; they are making ready to start.
So tell the men I am coming to,
To make themselves clean, inside and out.
To roll the grave-stone off their souls, from the cave of their bellies,
To prepare to be men.
Or else prepare for the other things.

SONG OF HUITZILOPOCHTLI

I am Huitzilopochtli,
The Red Huitzilopochtli,
The blood-red.

I am Huitzilopochtli,
Yellow of the sun,
Sun in the blood.

I am Huitzilopochtli,
White of the bone,
Bone in the blood.

I am Huitzilopochtli,
With a blade of grass between my teeth.

I am Huitzilopochtli, sitting in the dark.
With my redness staining the body of the dark.

I watch by the fire.
I wait behind men.

In the stillness of my night
The cactus sharpens his thorn.
The grass feels with his roots for the other sun.

Deeper than the roots of the mango tree
Down in the centre of the earth
Is the yellow, serpent-yellow shining of my sun.

Oh, beware of him!
Oh, beware of me!

Who runs athwart my serpent-flame
Gets bitten and must die.

I am the sleeping and the waking
Of the anger of the manhood of men.
I am the leaping and quaking
Of fire bent back again.

HUITZILOPOCHTLI'S WATCH

Red Huitzilopochtli
Keeps day and night apart.

Huitzilopochtli the golden
Guards life from death, and death from life.

No grey-dogs, cowards, pass him.
No spotted traitors crawl by,
False fair ones cannot slip through
Past him, from the one to the other.

Brave men have peace at nightfall,
True men look up at the dawn,
Men in their manhood walk out
Into blue day, past Huitzilopochtli.

Red Huitzilopochtli
Is the purifier.

Black Huitzilopochtli
Is doom.

Huitzilopochtli golden
Is the liberating fire.

White Huitzilopochtli
Is washed bone.

Green Huitzilopochtli
Is Malintzi's blade of grass.

Why is your hand so red, Huitzilopochtli?

With blood of slain men, Brother!

Must it always be red?

Till green-robed Malintzi brings her water-bowl.

The dead are on their journey, the way is dark.
There is only the Morning Star.
Beyond the white of whiteness,
Beyond the blackness of black,
Beyond spoken day,
Beyond the unspoken passion of night,
The light which is fed from two vessels
From the black oil and the white
Shines at the gate.

A gate to the innermost place
Where the Breath and the Fountains commingle,

Where the dead are living, and the living are dead.
The deeps that life cannot fathom,
The source and the End, of which we know
Only that it is, and its life is our life and our death.

All men cover their eyes
Before the unseen.
All men be lost in silence,
Within the noiseless.
Like the green candles of Malintzi
Like a new tree in new leaf.
The rain of blood is fallen, is gone into the earth.

The dead have gone the long journey
Beyond the star.
Huitzilopochtli has thrown his black mantle
To those who would sleep.
When the blue wind of Quetzalcoatl
Waves softly,
When the water of Malintzi falls
Making a greenness:
Count the red drains of the Huitzilopochtli
Fire in your hearts, Oh men.
And blow the ash away.

For the living live,
And the dead die.
But the fingers of all touch the fingers of all
In the Morning Star.

MY WAY IS NOT THY WAY

My way is not thy way, and thine is not mine.
But come, before we part
Let us separately go to the Morning Star,
And meet there.

I do not point you to my road, nor yet
Call: "Oh come!"
But the Star is the same for both of us,
Winsome.

The good ghost of me goes down the distance
To the Holy Ghost.
Oh you, in the tent of the cloven flame
Meet me, you I like most.

Each man his own way forever, but towards
The hoverer between;
Who opens his flame like a tent-flap,
As we slip in unseen.

A man cannot tread like a woman,
Nor a woman step out like a man.
The ghost of each through the leaves of shadow
Moves as it can.

But the Morning Star and the Evening Star
Pitch tents of flame
Where we foregather like gypsies, none knowing
How the other came.

I ask for nothing except to slip
In the tent of the Holy Ghost
And be there in the house of the cloven flame,
Guest of the Host.

Be with me there, my woman,
Be bodily there.
Then let the flame wrap round us
Like a snare.

Be there along with me, oh men!
Reach across the hearth,
And laugh with me, while the woman rests,
For all we are worth.

SONG OF DEATH

Sing the song of death, oh sing it!
For without the song of death, the song of life
becomes pointless and silly.

Sing then the song of death, and the longest journey
and what the soul carries with him, and what he leaves behind
and how he finds the darkness that enfolds him into utter
 peace
at last, at last, beyond innumerable seas.

Manuscript "*B*"

DEMIURGE

They say that reality exists only in the spirit
that corporal existence is a kind of death
that pure being is bodiless
that the idea of the form precedes the form substantial.

But what nonsense it is!
as if any Mind could have imagined a lobster
dozing the under-deeps, then reaching out a savage and iron
    claw!

Even the mind of God can only imagine
those things that have become themselves;
bodies and presences, here and now, creatures with a foothold
    in creation
even if it is only a lobster on tip-toe.

Religion knows better than philosophy
Religion knows that Jesus never was Jesus
till he was born from a womb, and ate soup and bread
and grew up, and became, in the wonder of creation, Jesus,
with a body and with needs, and a lovely spirit.

WHALES WEEP NOT!

They say the sea is cold, but the sea contains
the hottest blood of all, and the wildest, the most urgent.

All the whales in the wider deeps, hot are they, as they urge
on and on, and dive beneath the ice-bergs.

The right whales, the sperm-whales, the hammer-heads, the killers
there they blow, there they blow, hot wild white breath out of the sea!

And they rock and they rock, through the sensual ageless ages
on the depths of the seven seas,
and through the salt they reel with drunk delight
and in the tropics tremble they with love
and roll with massive, strong desire, like gods.
Then the great bull lies up against his bride
in the blue deep of the sea
as mountain pressing on mountain, in the zest of life:
and out of the inward roaring of the inner red ocean of whale blood
the long tip reaches strong, intense, like a maelstrom-tip, and comes to rest
in the clasp and the soft, wild clutch of a she-whale's fathomless body.

And over the bridge of the whale's strong phallus, linking the wonder of whales
the burning archangels under the sea keep passing, back and forth,
keep passing archangels of bliss
from him to her, from her to him, great Cherubim
that wait on whales in mid-ocean, suspended in the waves of the sea
great heaven of whales in the waters, old hierarchies.
And enormous mother whales lie dreaming suckling their whale-tender young

and dreaming with strange whale eyes wide open in the waters
    of the beginning and the end.

And bull-whales gather their women and whale-calves in a
    ring
when danger threatens, on the surface of the ceaseless flood
and range themselves like great fierce Seraphim facing the
    threat
encircling their huddled monsters of love.
and all this happiness in the sea, in the salt
where God is also love, but without words:
and Aphrodite is the wife of whales
most happy, happy she!
and Venus among the fishes skips and is a she-dolphin
she is the gay, delighted porpoise sporting with love and the
    sea
she is the female tunny-fish, round and happy among the males
and dense with happy blood, dark rainbow bliss in the sea.

GLORY OF DARKNESS

Blue and dark
Bavarian gentians, tall ones
make a dark blue gloom
in the sunny room

They have added blueness to blueness, until
it is dark; beauty

blue joy of my soul
Bavarian gentians
your dark blue gloom is so noble!

How deep I have gone
dark gentians
since I embarked on your dark blue fringes
how deep, how deep, how happy!

What a journey for my soul
in the dark blue gloom
of gentians here in the sunny room!

BAVARIAN GENTIANS

Not every man has gentians in his house
In soft September, at slow, sad Michaelmas.

Bavarian gentians, tall and dark, but dark
Darkening the day-time torch-like with the smoking blueness
    of Pluto's gloom,
Ribbed hellish flowers erect, with their blaze of darkness
    spread blue
Blown into points, by the heavy white draught of the day.

Torch-flowers of the blue-smoking darkness, Pluto's dark
    blue blaze
Black lamps from the halls of Dio, smoking dark blue
Giving off darkness, blue darkness, upon Demeter's yellow-
    pale day

Reach me a gentian, give me a torch!
Let me guide myself with the blue, forked torch of a flower
Down the darker and darker stairs, where blue is darkened on
blueness
Down the way Persephone goes, just now, in first-frosted
September
To the sightless realm where darkness is married to dark
And Persephone herself is but a voice, as a bride
A gloom invisible enfolded in the deeper dark
Of the arms of Pluto as he ravishes her once again
And pierces her once more with his passion of the utter dark.

Among the splendour of black-blue torches, shedding fathomless darkness on the nuptials.

Give me a flower on a tall stem, and three dark flames,
For I will go to the wedding, and be wedding-guest
At the marriage of the living dark.

Version of Manuscript "A"

DEATH IS NOT EVIL, EVIL IS MECHANICAL

Only the human being, absolved from kissing and strife
goes on and on and on, without wandering
fixed upon the hub of the ego
going, yet never wandering, fixed, yet in motion,
the kind of hell that is real, grey and awful
sinless and stainless going round and round
the kind of hell grey Dante never saw
but of which he had a bit inside him.

Know thyself, and that thou art mortal.
But know thyself, denying that thou art mortal:
a thing of kisses and strife
a lit-up shaft of rain
a calling column of blood
a rose tree bronzey with thorns
a mixture of yea and nay
a rainbow of love and hate
a wind that blows back and forth
a creature of conflict, like a cataract:
know thyself, in denial of all these things.

And thou shalt begin to spin round on the hub of the obscene
ego
a grey void thing that goes without wandering
a machine that in itself is nothing
a centre of the evil world.

THE SHIP OF DEATH

I

Now it is autumn and the falling fruit
and the long journey towards oblivion.

The apples falling like great drops of dew
to bruise themselves an exit from themselves.

And it is time to go, to bid farewell
to one's own self, and find an exit
from the fallen self.

II

Have you built your ship of death, O have you?
O build your ship of death, for you will need it.

The grim frost is at hand, when the apples will fall
thick, almost thundrous, on the hardened earth.

And death is on the air like a smell of ashes!
Ah! can't you smell it?
And in the bruised body, the frightened soul
finds itself shrinking, wincing from the cold
that blows upon it through the orifices.

III

And can a man his own quietus make
with a bare bodkin?

With daggers, bodkins, bullets, man can make
a bruise or break of exit for his life;
but is that a quietus, O tell me, is it quietus?

Surely not so! for how could murder, even self-murder
ever a quietus make?

IV

O let us talk of quiet that we know,
that we can know, the deep and lovely quiet
of a strong heart at peace!

How can we this, our own quietus, make?

V

Build then the ship of death, for you must take
the longest journey, to oblivion.

And die the death, the long and painful death
that lies between the old self and the new.

Already our bodies are fallen, bruised, badly bruised,
already our souls are oozing through the exit
of the cruel bruise.

Already the dark and endless ocean of the end
is washing in through the breaches of our wounds,
already the flood is upon us.

O build your ship of death, your little ark
and furnish it with food, with little cakes, and wine
for the dark flight down oblivion.

VI

Piecemeal the body dies, and the timid soul
has her footing washed away, as the dark flood rises.

We are dying, we are dying, we are all of us dying
and nothing will stay the death-flood rising within us
and soon it will rise on the world, on the outside world.

We are dying, we are dying, piecemeal our bodies are dying
and our strength leaves us,
and our soul cowers naked in the dark rain over the flood,
cowering in the last branches of the tree of our life.

VII

We are dying, we are dying, so all we can do
is now to be willing to die, and to build the ship
of death to carry the soul on the longest journey.

A little ship, with oars and food
and little dishes, and all accoutrements
fitting and ready for the departing soul.

Now launch the small ship, now as the body dies
and life departs, launch out, the fragile soul
in the fragile ship of courage, the ark of faith
with its store of food and little cooking pans
and change of clothes,
upon the flood's black waste
upon the waters of the end

upon the sea of death, where still we sail
darkly, for we cannot steer, and have no port.

There is no port, there is nowhere to go
only the deepening blackness darkening still
blacker upon the soundless, ungurgling flood
darkness at one with darkness, up and down
and sideways utterly dark, so there is no direction any more
and the little ship is there; yet she is gone.
She is not seen, for there is nothing to see her by.
She is gone! gone! and yet
somewhere she is there.
Nowhere!

VIII

And everything is gone, the body is gone
completely under, gone, entirely gone.
The upper darkness is heavy as the lower,
between them the little ship
is gone

It is the end, it is oblivion.

IX

And yet out of eternity a thread
separates itself on the blackness,
a horizontal thread
that fumes a little with pallor upon the dark.

Is it illusion? or does the pallor fume
a little higher?
Ah wait, wait, for there's the dawn,
the cruel dawn of coming back to life
out of oblivion.

Wait, wait, the little ship
drifting, beneath the deathly ashy grey
of a flood-dawn.

Wait, wait! even so, a flush of yellow
and strangely, O chilled wan soul, a flush of rose.

A flush of rose, and the whole thing starts again.

X

The flood subsides, and the body, like a worn sea-shell
emerges strange and lovely.
And the little ship wings home, faltering and lapsing
on the pink flood,
and the frail soul steps out, into the house again
filling the heart with peace.

Swings the heart renewed with peace
even of oblivion.

Oh build your ship of death. Oh build it!
for you will need it.
For the voyage of oblivion awaits you.

THE END, THE BEGINNING

If there were not an utter and absolute dark
of silence and sheer oblivion
at the core of everything,
how terrible the sun would be,
how ghastly it would be to strike a match, and make a light.

But the very sun himself is pivoted
upon the core of pure oblivion,
so is a candle, even as a match.

And if there were not an absolute, utter forgetting
and a ceasing to know, a perfect ceasing to know
and a silent, sheer cessation of all awareness
how terrible life would be!
how terrible it would be to think and know, to have consciousness!

But dipped, once dipped in dark oblivion
the soul has peace, inward and lovely peace.

A CHRONOLOGY

Some of the main events of Lawrence's life

1885	September 11, David Herbert Lawrence born, son of John Arthur Lawrence, collier ("coal miner" in USA), and Lydia, née Beardsall, schoolteacher, at Victoria Street, Eastwood, Nottinghamshire, the fourth child of five, three boys and two girls.
1898	Awarded scholarship at Nottingham high school.
1901	Left high school for job with firm of surgical goods manufacturers, described in *Sons and Lovers.*
1902	At British School, Eastwood, Notts., as pupil-teacher.
1903	Attended Nottingham University College. Began *The White Peacock.*
1905	Taught at Davidson Road School, Croydon. The Miriam poems, many others, articles, short stories, finished *The White Peacock.* Met Ford Madox Hueffer, who took a very active interest in him.
1909	*Collected Letters,* the best source material on his life, begin. Heinemann's accepted, via Hueffer, *The White Peacock.*
1910	His mother died, of cancer. Several poems on her last illness and death.
1911	*The White Peacock* published. Met Edward Garnett. The Helen poems must have been written about this period.

1912 *The Trespasser* published by Duckworth. Met Frieda Von Richthofen, at that time married. Travelled in Germany, mostly in the Rhineland and Bavaria.

1913 *Love Poems and Others* published by Duckworth. *Sons and Lovers* published by Duckworth. Returned to England, back to Munich, thence to Lerici, Italy. Lawrence is now a famous writer.

1914 Returned to England. Married to Frieda. *The Prussian Officer* published by Duckworth. Lived at Chesham, Bucks.

1915 Moved to Pulborough, Sussex. Around this time he must have met most of his friends of that time, Middleton Murry, "Brett," Katherine Mansfield, Koteliansky, "Peter Warlock," "Michael Arlen," Bertrand Russell, Lady Ottoline Morrell. Richard and Hilda Aldington. *The Rainbow* published and suppressed. A magazine, *The Signature*, with Lawrence, Murry and Mansfield as editors, ran for three issues. Moved to Hampstead, moved to Cornwall.

1916 *Twilight in Italy* and *Amore* published by Duckworth.

1917 Expelled from Cornwall as suspicious person. Moved to London.

1918 Moved to Newbury, Berks., thence to Middleton-by-Wirksworth, Derbyshire, thence back to Newbury.

1919 Moved to Italy, first Florence, then Capri, then, early in 1920

1920 to Taormina, Sicily. Private edition of *Women in Love*, New York.

1921 *Women in Love* published by Secker. Travelled, Baden-Baden, Zell-am-See bei Salzburg, back to Sicily, then to Sardinia. *Sea and Sardinia* published by Selzer, New York.

1922 Travelled, Ceylon, Australia, Tahiti, San Francisco. *Aaron's Rod* published, by Selzer, then Secker. From San Francisco to Taos, New Mexico, to the ranch of Mabel Dodge, thence to

1923 Mexico, with Witter Bynner. At the height of his productivity, *Kangaroo, Birds, Beasts and Flowers, Maestro Don Gesualdo*, published. *Mornings in Mexico, The Plumed Serpent, The Woman Who Rode Away*, all in process. *The Boy in the Bush, Fantasia of the Unconscious* finished. Back to England at the end of November.

1924 Travelled, Baden-Baden, Paris, London, back to Taos, New Mexico. Thence to Oaxaca. Completed the Mexican material begun earlier in Mexico City and Guadalajara. In Oaxaca Lawrence was ill and Frieda discovered that what he referred to as a "bronchial condition" was tuberculosis.

1925 Back to Taos, thence to London, thence to Baden-Baden, thence to Spotorno, Italy. *The Plumed Serpent* published by Secker.

1926–28 Villa Mirenda, Scandicci, Italy, except for trips to Germany, England and Switzerland. *Lady Chatterley's Lover*, privately printed. Friendship with Aldous and Maria Huxley.

1928	Travel in Germany, Switzerland, France. At Bandol, Var, France, until March 1929.
1929	More travel, Paris, Florence, Mallorca. Lawrence's paintings exhibited in London, the show closed by censorship. *Pansies* published, in private edition, and by Secker. Lawrence in these years since Mexico was getting steadily more ill, and in 1930
1930	while at Bandol, became gravely ill and moved to a sanatorium at Vence, in the hills nearby. On March 2nd, he died, and was buried in the local cemetery, his grave marked with the phoenix he had designed for himself. Later his ashes were brought to a little chapel on the mountainside ranch above Taos.